Mario F. Triola

Minitab® Manual
Elementary Statistics

Custom Edition

Taken from:
Minitab® Manual: Elementary Statistics, Thirteenth Edition
by Mario F. Triola

Taken from:

Minitab® Manual: Elementary Statistics, Thirteenth Edition
by Mario F. Triola
Copyright © 2018, 2014, 2010 by Pearson Education, Inc.
New York, New York 10013

Pearson Education, Inc., 330 Hudson Street, New York, New York 10013
A Pearson Education Company
www.pearsoned.com

Printed in the United States of America

6   17

000200010272103608

GM

ISBN 10: 1-323-76417-8
ISBN 13: 978-1-323-76417-6

Preface

This *Minitab Manual,* 13th edition, is a supplement to textbooks in the Triola Statistics Series (listed below) and *Statistical Reasoning for Everyday Life* by Bennett, Briggs, and Triola.

Triola Statistics Series

Elementary Statistics, Thirteenth Edition

Essentials of Statistics, Sixth Edition

Elementary Statistics Using Excel, Sixth Edition

Elementary Statistics Using the TI-83/84 Calculator, Fifth Edition

Biostatistics for the Biological and Health Sciences, Second Edition

This manual is based on Minitab Release 17, but it can also be used with other versions of Minitab. Many exercises in the textbook and this manual use datasets that can be downloaded was Minitab worksheets. To download these Minitab worksheets, go to the website www.TriolaStats.com.

Here are major objectives of this manual/workbook and the Minitab software:

- Describe how Minitab can be used for the methods of statistics presented in the textbook. Specific and detailed procedures for using Minitab are included, along with examples of Minitab screen displays.

- Involve students with a spreadsheet type of software application, which will help them work with other spreadsheet programs they will encounter in their professional work.

- Incorporate an important component of computer usage without using valuable class time required for concepts of statistics.

- Replace tedious calculations with computer results so students can focus on understanding and interpreting results.

- Apply alternative methods, such as simulations or bootstrapping methods that are made possible with computer usage.

- Include topics, such as analysis of variance and multiple regression, that require calculations so complex that they realistically cannot be done without computer software.

It should be emphasized that this manual/workbook is designed to be a *supplement* to textbooks in the Triola Statistics Series; it is not designed to be a self-contained statistics textbook. It is assumed throughout this manual/workbook that the theory, assumptions, and procedures of statistics are described in the textbook that is used.

Chapter 1 of this supplement describes some of the important basics for using Minitab. Chapters 2 through 14 in this manual/workbook correspond to Chapters 2 through 14 in *Elementary Statistics*, 13th edition. However, the individual chapter *sections* in this manual/workbook generally do *not* match the sections in the textbook. Each chapter includes a description of the Minitab procedures relevant to the corresponding chapter in the textbook. This cross-referencing makes it very easy to use this supplement with the textbook.

Chapters include illustrations of Minitab procedures as well as detailed steps describing the use of those procedures. It would be helpful to follow the steps shown in these sections so the basic procedures will become familiar. You can compare your own computer display to the display given in this supplement and then verify that your procedure works correctly. You can then proceed to conduct the experiments that follow.

We welcome any comments or suggestions that you might have for improving this Minitab manual/workbook. Please send them to the Pearson Statistics Editor.

The author and publisher are very grateful to Minitab, Inc. for the continuing support and cooperation.

M.F.T.
Madison, CT
January, 2017

Contents

1
Basics
of Minitab

1-1 Starting Minitab

Minitab Release 17 is the latest version available as of this writing. It can be purchased and downloaded online. As this manual was being written, students can rent Minitab or Minitab Express for $29.99 for a semester. (Go to www.Minitab.com, select Minitab 17, and select the Academic Pricing option.)

System Requirements System requirements include the following: Windows 7 Service Pack 1 or higher or Windows 8 or 8.1 or Windows 10, 512 MB RAM (1 GB recommended), 2 GB hard disk space available, display with resolution of 1024 x 768 or higher, Internet connection for activation of single-user licenses.

Starting Minitab: With Minitab installed, you can start it by clicking on the Minitab icon on the startup screen.

You can also start Minitab as follows:

  1.   Click on the taskbar item of **Start**.

  2.   Select **Programs**.

  3.   Select **Minitab 17** (or whatever Minitab release you are using).

  4.   Select **Minitab**.

Session/Data Windows   After opening Minitab, you should see a display of its two main windows: the Session window and the Data window (as shown on the top of the following page). The Session window displays results and it also allows you to enter commands. The top of the display on the following page consists of the Session window. The Data window, shown on the bottom of the display on the following page, consists of a spreadsheet for entering data in columns. These spreadsheets are called *worksheets* in Minitab. Minitab allows you to have multiple worksheets in different Data windows.

Session and Data Windows

1-2 Downloading Worksheets

Data entered in Minitab can be saved as a worksheet (with an extension of .MTW) or a project file (with an extension of .MPJ).

Worksheet: Spreadsheet containing columns of data

Project: File containing all work created during a session, including worksheets, graphs, and session window output.

This manual/workbook and the stored Minitab data files all refer to *worksheets*.

Downloading Minitab Worksheets from www.TriolaStats.com

The website accessed at www.TriolaStats.com includes Minitab worksheets containing the data sets in Appendix B from the textbook. For example, Data Set 1 "Body Data" in Appendix B of the textbook includes body and exam measurements from 300 adult subjects. That data set is available as the Minitab *worksheet* Body Data.MTW. The extension MTW shows us that this file is a Minitab worksheet, not a Minitab project. Details about the data sets are included in Appendix B of the textbook. For example, Appendix B shows that the column labeled *Systolic* is systolic blood pressure with units of mm Hg. Here is the procedure for downloading a Minitab worksheet from the website www.TriolaStats.com.

Downloading a Minitab Worksheet from www.TriolaStats.com

Go to www.TriolaStats.com and click on **Stat Resources.** Proceed to select **Data Sets,** then select **Appendix B Data Sets,** then click on the Minitab icon. All of the data sets in Appendix B can then be downloaded.

Opening a Minitab Worksheet

1.   Once the data sets have been downloaded, open Minitab, then click on **File**.

2.   Click on the subdirectory item of **Open** then navigate to the file containing the downloaded Minitab data sets.

3.   You should now see a window that includes the list shown below.

4.   Click on the name of the worksheet that you want to open.

5.   Click on the **Open** button.

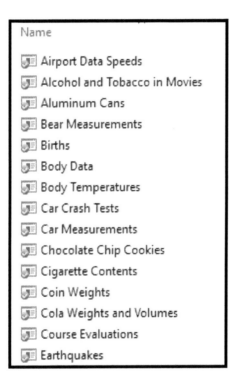

1-3 Entering Data

In Minitab, there are three types of data: (1) *numeric* data (numbers), (2) *text* data (characters), and (3) *date/time* data. We will work mostly with numeric data. Also, data can be in the form of a column, a stored constant, or a matrix. We will work with *columns* of data. Shown below is a typical Minitab screen. We have entered data values in the first four columns identified as C1, C2, C3, and C4. Because the entries in the first column consists of *text* data, the first column becomes C1-T. We have also entered the column names of "Airport Code," "Verizon," and so on. (See Data Set 32 in Appendix B of the textbook.)

Entry of sample data is very easy. Click on the first cell on the desired column, type an entry, then press the **Enter** key. Then type a second entry and press the **Enter** key again. Continue until all of the sample data have been entered. If you make a mistake, simply click on the wrong entry and type the correct value and press **Enter**.

Airport Data Speeds.MTW ***				
↓	C1-T	C2	C3	C4	C5
	Airport Code	Verizon	Sprint	ATT	TMobile
1	RSW	38.5	13.0	9.7	8.6
2	ORD	55.6	30.4	8.2	7.0
3	SNA	22.4	15.2	7.1	18.5
4	MEM	14.1	2.4	14.4	16.7
5	MKE	23.1	2.7	13.4	5.6
6	IND	24.5	2.1	30.6	3.2
7	DCA	6.5	0.8	14.4	16.2
8	LAS	21.5	1.6	17.0	6.9
9	CMH	25.7	5.6	3.8	27.3
10	PIT	14.7	4.0	12.4	10.1
11	ATL	77.8	0.4	33.9	27.3
12	MDW	71.3	2.5	5.5	13.3
13	BWI	43.0	3.4	12.7	3.2
14	RDU	20.2	2.7	11.0	5.4
15	FLL	15.5	10.6	4.8	4.3
16	SMF	13.7	0.3	17.5	23.5

Naming columns: It is wise to enter a name for the different columns of data, so that it becomes easy to keep track of data sets with meaningful names. See the preceding display that includes these column names: Airport Code, Verizon, Sprint, ATT, and TMobile.

1-4 Saving Data

After entering one or more columns of data, you can *save* all of the data as a Minitab worksheet, which is a file with an extension of .MTW. Use the following procedure.

Minitab Procedure for Saving a Worksheet

1. Click on the main menu item of **File**.
2. Click on **Save Worksheet As ....**.
3. In the top box of the dialog box, select the desired location of where you want the Minitab worksheet saved. In the "Save as type" box, enter the desired name of the file. The extension of .MTW will be automatically provided by Minitab.
4. Click on **Save**.

Note: For saved worksheets, Minitab is *forward* compatible, but not *backward* compatible. For example, a worksheet saved in Minitab Release 16 format is not compatible with Minitab Release 15 and earlier releases of Minitab, but a worksheet saved in a Minitab Release 14 format can be opened and used in Minitab 14, Minitab 15, Minitab 16, and later releases.

1-5 Printing

We have noted that Minitab involves a screen with two separate parts: (1) The Session window at the top and (2) the Data window at the bottom. The contents of the Session window and Data window can be printed as follows.

Printing the Session Window or Data Window

1. *Session window:* If you want to print the session (top) window portion of the screen, click anywhere on the session window.

   Data window: If you want to print the data (bottom) portion of the screen, click on any cell in the Data window.

2. Click on the main menu item of **File**.

3. Click on **Print Session Window** or **Print Worksheet**. (You will see only one of these two options. The option that you see is the result of the choice you made in Step 1. If you see "Print Worksheet" but you want to print the Session window, go back to Step 1 and click on the Session window portion of the screen.)

4. If you select Print Worksheet in Step 3, you will get a dialog box. Enter your preferences, then click **OK**.

Printing a Large Data Set in a Word Processor

Some data sets are so large that they cannot be printed on a few pages. If you enter or somehow create a data set with thousands of values, printing would require many pages. One way to circumvent that problem is to move the data to a word processor where the values can be reconfigured for easier printing. Follow these steps.

1. With the data set displayed in the data window, click on the value at the top. Hold the mouse button down and drag the mouse to the bottom of the data set, then release it so that the entire list of values is highlighted.

2. Click on **Edit**, then click on **Copy Cells**.

3. Now go into your word processor and click on **Edit**, then **Paste**. The entire list of values will be in your word processing document where you can configure them as you please. For example, you might press **End**, then press the **space bar**, then press the **Del** key. The second value will be moved up to the top row. Repeat this process to rearrange the data in multiple rows and columns (instead of one really large column).

1-6 Manipulating Data (Sort, Stack, Unstack, Transpose)

Sorting Data

There is often a need to *sort* data. Data are sorted when they are arranged in order from low to high (or from high to low). Identification of outliers becomes easier with a sorted list of values.

Minitab Procedure for Sorting Data

1. Enter the data or open a worksheet with data.

2. Click on the main menu item of **Data.**

3. Click on the subdirectory item of **Sort.**

4. You will now see a dialog box like the one shown below. In the "Columns to sort by" box, enter the column that you want used as the basis for sorting. In the "Columns to sort" box, select either "Specified columns" or "All columns." In the box labelled "Storage location for the columns," click on the triangle at the right and choose among the six options. The dialog box shown below indicates the option of "At the end of the current worksheet," which is often a good choice. The entries shown below tell Minitab to sort the pulse rates (in column C3) and store the sorted list after column C15. Click **OK** after completing the dialog box.

Stacking Data

We sometimes want to take two or more columns of data and "stack" or combine them into a single column.

Minitab Procedure for Stacking Columns Into One Column

1.   Enter the data or open a worksheet with data.

2.   Click on the main menu item of **Data.**

3.   Click on the subdirectory item of **Stack**.

4.   Select **Columns.**

5.   You will now see a dialog box like the one shown below. This dialog box tells Minitab to stack the data from columns C5 through C10 and put them into column C15. (In this case, it would make no sense to stack these particular columns, but stacking makes sense in other cases.) Click **OK.**

Unstacking Data

We sometimes want to take one column and break it up into two or more columns. In addition to the column to be unstacked, we need another column with entries that will be used as the basis for unstacking. For example, consider the "Body Data" dataset in Appendix B. That dataset lists genders in column C2 and it lists heights in column C12. If we want to take the column of 300 heights and separate it into two columns based on gender, we can use Minitab's unstacking feature to accomplish that.

Minitab Procedure for Unstacking a Column Into Two or More Columns

1.   Enter the data or open a worksheet with data.

2.   Click on the main menu item of **Data.**

3.   Click on the subdirectory item of **Unstack Columns**.

4.   You will now see a dialog box like the one shown below. This dialog box tells Minitab to unstack the column of heights using the column of genders as the basis for unstacking. The result will be that two new columns will be formed: (1) heights of females; (2) heights of males.

Transposing Data

"Transposing" data involves taking select rows and reconfiguring them as columns, or vice versa. This can be really helpful when we import data from some other source but the data are arranged in rows and we need to have the data arranged in columns.

Minitab Procedure for Transposing Data

1.   Enter the data or open a worksheet with data.

2.   Click on the main menu item of **Data.**

3.   Click on the subdirectory item of **Transpose Columns**.

4.   You will now see a dialog box like the one shown below. This dialog box tells Minitab to take the data in columns C1 through C20 and reconfigure them to be in rows instead of columns. Because "After last column in use" is selected, the reconfigured data will be in rows following the last column of data.

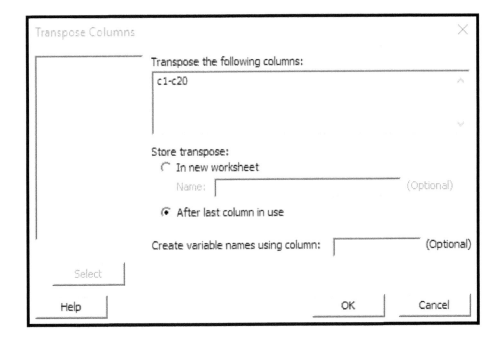

1-7 Command Editor and Transforming Data

Data may be *transformed* with operations such as adding a constant, multiplying by a constant, or using functions such as logarithm (common or natural), sine, exponential, or absolute value. For example, if you have a data set consisting of temperatures on the Fahrenheit scale (such as the body temperatures in the Minitab data set Body Temperatures) and you want to transform the values to the Celsius scale, you can use the equation

$$C = \frac{5}{9}(F - 32)$$

Such transformations can be accomplished by using Minitab's *command editor* or by using Minitab's virtual calculator.

Using Command Editor to Transform Data

1. Click on the Session window portion of the screen. (The Session window is on the top portion; the Data window is the bottom portion.)

2. Click on **Editor**.

3. Click on **Enable Commands**.

4. You should now see **MTB >** and you can enter a command. The command

    LET C2 = (5/9)*(C1 − 32)

    tells Minitab to take the values in column C1, subtract 32 from each value, then multiply by the fraction 5/9. This expression corresponds to the above formula for converting Fahrenheit temperatures to the Celsius scale. The temperatures on the Fahrenheit scale of 98.6, 98.6, 98.0, 97.3, and 97.2 are converted to these temperatures on the Celsius scale: 37.0000, 37.0000, 36.6667, 36.2778, and 36.2222.

Using Minitab's Calculator to Transform Data

You can also click on **Calc**, then **Calculator** to get a virtual calculator that allows you to create new columns by performing operations with existing columns. The display below shows that column C10 will be the result of converting the temperatures in column C3 from the Fahrenheit scale to the Celsius scale. The expression shown below indicates that 32 is subtracted from each entry in column C3, then the result is multiplied by 5/9. Click **OK** when done.

1-8 Closing Worksheets and Exiting Minitab

Closing worksheets: You can close the current *worksheet* by clicking on ✕ located at the upper right corner of the *worksheet window*. If you click on ✕, you will be told that the data in the worksheet will be removed and this action cannot be undone. You will be given the opportunity to save the data in a separate file, or you can click **No** to close the window. The Minitab program will continue to be active, even though you have just closed the current worksheet.

Exiting Minitab: Had enough for now? To exit or quit the Minitab program, click on ✕ located in the extreme upper right corner. Another way to exit Minitab is to click on **File**, then click on **Exit**. You will be asked if you want to save changes to a project before closing. This is your last chance to save items that you want saved. Assuming that you are finished and you want to exit Minitab, click **No**.

1-9 Exchanging Data with Other Applications

There may be times when you want to move data from Minitab to another application (such as Excel or STATDISK or Microsoft Word) or to move data from another application to Minitab. *Instead of manually retyping all of the data values, you can usually transfer the data set directly.* Given below are two ways to accomplish this. The first of the following two procedures is easier, if it works (and it often does work).

Method 1: Use Copy/Paste

1. With the data set displayed in the source program, use the mouse to highlight the values that you want to copy. (Click on the first value, then hold the mouse button down and drag it to highlight all of the values, then release the mouse button.)

2. While still in the source program, click on **Edit**, then click on **Copy**.

3. Now go into Minitab and click on **Edit**, then **Paste**. The entire list of values should appear in Minitab.

Method 2: Use Text Files

1. In the software program containing the original set of data, create a text file of the data. [In Minitab you can create a text file by clicking on **File**, then **Save Worksheet As**, then enter the file name near the bottom, then click on **Save as type** and select the desired format, such as use Text (ANSI) or Text (Unicode).]

2. Minitab and most other major applications allow you to import the text file that was created. (To import a text file into Minitab, click on **File**, then **Open,** then click on **All Minitab Files** and select **Text**.)

CHAPTER 1 EXPERIMENTS: Basics of Minitab

1-1. ***Entering Sample Data*** When first experimenting with procedures for using Minitab, it's a good strategy to use a small data set instead of one that is large. If a small data set is lost, you can easily enter it a second time. In this experiment, we will enter a small data set, save it, retrieve it, and print it. The "Body Temperatures" data set from Appendix B of the Triola textbook includes these body temperatures, along with others:

98.6   98.6   98.0   98.0   99.0

    a.   Open Minitab and enter the above sample values in column C1. (See the procedure described in Section 1-4 of this manual/workbook.)

    b.   Save the worksheet using the worksheet name of TEMP (because the values are body temperatures). See the procedure described in Section 1-3 of this manual/workbook.

    c.   Print the data set by printing the display of the data window.

    d.   Exit Minitab, then restart it and retrieve the worksheet named TEMP. Save another copy of the same data set using the file name of TEMP2. Print TEMP2 and include the title at the top.

1-2. ***Downloading and Opening a Worksheet*** The Minitab worksheet Body Data.MTW is in Appendix B of the textbook. It lists ages body and exam measurements from 300 subjects. The Minitab worksheet is already available at www.TriolaStats.com. Open the worksheet Body Data.MTW (see Section 1-2 of this manual/workbook), then print its contents.

1-3. ***Generating Random Data*** In addition to entering or downloading data, Minitab can also *generate* data sets. In this experiment, we will use Minitab to simulate 50 births.
a. Select **Calc** from the main menu bar, then select **Random Data.**
b. Select **Integer**, because we want whole numbers.
c. Enter 50 for the number of values, enter the column (such as C1) to be used for the data, enter 0 for minimum, and enter 1 for the maximum, then click **OK**.
d. Examine the displayed values and count the number of times that 1 occurs. Record the result here: _____ If we stipulate that a 0 simulates the birth of a girl and 1 simulates the birth of a boy, this experiment simulates 50 births and results in the number of girls.

1-4. ***Generating Random Data*** Experiment 1-3 results in the random generation of the digits 0 and 1. Minitab can also generate sample data from other types of populations. In this experiment, we will use Minitab to simulate the random selection of 50 IQ scores.
a. Select **Calc** from the main menu bar, then select **Random Data.**
b. Select **Normal**. (The normal distribution is described in the textbook.)
c. Enter 50 for the number of values, enter the column (such as C1) to be used for the data, enter 100 for the mean, and enter 15 for the standard deviation. (These statistics are described in the textbook.) Click **OK** and print the results.

1-5.   ***Saving a Worksheet*** Listed below are pulse rates of females (from the "Body Data" dataset in Appendix B.) Manually enter these pulse rates in column C1 and name that column Pulse Rate. Save the worksheet with the name Pulse. Print the worksheet.

Female Pulse Rates
78 80 68 56 76 78 78   90 96 60 98 66 100 76 64 82 62 72 78 74
90 90 68 72 82 72 78 104 62 72 72 88   74 72 82 78 78 98 72 64

1-6.   ***Saving a Worksheet*** Listed below are arrival delay times (minutes) for American Airline flights from New York to Los Angeles. Negative values correspond to flights that arrived early. Enter the data in three columns of a Minitab worksheet, and give the columns meaningful names. Save the worksheet with the name "Flights." Print the worksheet.

Flight 1	−32	−25	−26	−6	5	−15	−17	−36
Flight 19	−5	−32	−13	−9	−19	49	−30	−23
Flight 21	−23	28	103	−19	−5	−46	13	−3

1-7.   ***Transforming Data*** Experiment 1-1 results in saving the worksheet TEMP that contains 5 body temperatures in degrees Fahrenheit. Retrieve that data set, then proceed to transform the temperatures to the Celsius scale. Store the Celsius temperatures in column C2. (See Section 1-7 in this manual/workbook.) Print the worksheet containing the original Fahrenheit temperatures in column C1 and the corresponding Celsius temperatures in column C2.

1-8.   ***Working Around Missing Data*** This project is based on the Technology Project for Chapter 1 in the textbook. We want to download a data set and manipulate it to work around missing data. First, download the "Body Temperatures" dataset in Appendix B from www.TriolaStats.com/ES13. Some statistical procedures, such as those involved with correlation and regression (discussed in later chapters) require data that consist of matched pairs of values, and those procedures ignore pairs in which at least one of the data values in a matched pair is missing. Assume that we want to conduct analyses for correlation and regression on the last two columns of data in the "Body Temperatures" dataset: Body temperatures measured at 8 AM on day 2 and again at 12 AM on day 2. For those last two columns, identify the rows with at least one missing value. Use Minitab's Sort feature that allows you to rearrange all rows using one particular column as the basis for sorting. First use the Sort feature to rearrange *all* rows using the "Day2_8AM" column as the basis for sorting (so that all missing values in the "Day2_8AM" column are at the end), then highlight and *delete* all of those rows with missing values in the "Day2_8AM" column. Next, use the Sort feature to rearrange all rows using the "Day2_12AM" column as the basis for sorting (so that all missing values in the "Day2_12AM" column are at the beginning), then highlight and *delete* all of those rows with missing values in the "12 AM day 2" column. The remaining rows will include matched pairs of body temperatures, and those rows will not include any missing values in the last two columns. Print the resulting reconfigured dataset.

1-9.   *Unstacking Data*   Download and open the "Body Data" dataset in Appendix B and proceed to "unstack" the heights into two columns, with one column containing the heights of females and the second column containing the heights of males. List the first 10 values in each column:

Female heights: _____

Male heights: _____

1-10.   *Stacking Data*   Download and open the "M&M Weights" dataset in Appendix B and proceed to stack all of the columns so that the 100 weights are in the same column. Print the column containing all of the 100 weights.

1-11.   *Sorting Data*   Download and open the "M&M Weights" dataset in Appendix B and proceed to sort only the column of weights of red M&Ms. List them here:

_____

_____

_____

1-12.   *Sorting Data*   Enter the following pulse rates in two rows as they are shown here. Then *transpose* these data so that they are in two columns. Print the two columns. Then stack the two columns so that all of the pulse rates are in the same column, and print that column.

Female Pulse Rates
78 80 68 56 76 78 78   90 96 60 98 66 100 76 64 82 62 72 78 74
90 90 68 72 82 72 78 104 62 72 72 88   74 72 82 78 78 98 72 64

2
Summarizing and Graphing Data

Important note: The topics of this chapter require that you use Minitab to enter data in a worksheet, retrieve worksheets, save worksheets, and print results, as described in Chapter 1 of this manual/ workbook.

2-1   Frequency Distributions

Section 2-1 in the textbook describes the construction of a table representing the *frequency distribution* for a set of data. The Appendix B data set "IQ and Lead" includes the following full IQ scores of subjects from the low lead group. (The "IQ and Lead" data set is available as a Minitab worksheet and it can be downloaded from www.TriolaStats.com as described in Section 1-2 of this manual/workbook.) The listing of IQ scores is followed by a table that is a frequency distribution summarizing the listed IQ scores.

Full IQ Scores of Low Lead Group

70 85 86 76 84 96 94 56 115 97 77 128 99 80 118 86 141 88 96 96
107 86 80 107 101 91 125 96 99 99 115 106 105 96 50 99 85 88 120 93
87 98 78 100 105 87 94 89 80 111 104 85 94 75 73 76 107 88 89 96
72 97 76 107 104 85 76 95 86 89 76 96 101 108 102 77 74 92

IQ Scores of Low Lead Group

IQ Score	Frequency
50 – 69	2
70 – 89	33
90 – 109	35
110 – 129	7
130 – 149	1

Minitab does not have a specific feature for generating a frequency distribution as in the table above, but the following procedure can be very helpful in constructing such a table.

Procedure for Counting Individual Data Values

  1.   Enter the data in a column of the Minitab worksheet (or open the Minitab worksheet "IQ and Lead" that includes the data).

  2.   Click on **Stat,** then click on **Tables**.

  3.   Select **Tally Individual Variables**.

  4.   Enter the column name in the box labeled "Variables." If the Minitab worksheet "IQ and Lead" has been downloaded and opened, the

  5.   In the pop-up window, select the option of **Counts**.

  6.   Click **OK**.

If the preceding IQ scores are used, the first few lines of the result are as shown below.

IQ FULL	Count
50	1
56	1
70	1
72	1
73	1
74	1
75	1
76	5
77	2
78	1
80	3
84	1
etc.	

With these tally counts, it is much easier to construct the frequency distribution in the format of the table on the preceding page. For example, it is easy to see from this tally list that there are 2 data values falling in the first class of 50–69.

Another way to obtain the frequency distribution is to generate a stemplot as described in Section 2-4 of this manual/workbook. The frequency counts needed for the frequency distribution can be identified by simply counting the number of digits to the right of each stem.

2-2 Histograms

Textbooks in the Triola textbook series describe histograms and provide detailed procedures for constructing them. It is noted that a histogram is an excellent device for exploring the *distribution* of a data set.

Minitab Procedure for a Histogram

1. Enter the data in a Minitab column, such as column C1. If the data are already stored in a Minitab worksheet, open the worksheet using the procedure described in Section 1-2 of this manual/workbook.

2. Click on the main menu item of **Graph**.

3. Select **Histogram** from the subdirectory.

4. Click on the option of **Simple**, then click **OK**.

5. In the dialog box, click on the column with the data so that the column label (such as C8) or the data name (IQ FULL) appears in the box as shown.

Generating a Histogram

6. Using Minitab with the full IQ scores in the "IQ and Lead" data set results in the following default histogram. This default Minitab-generated histogram can be edited by double-clicking on the attribute that you want to change. To change the horizontal scale to use your own class limits, double-click on the *x*-axis and use the pop-up window to change the scale. For example, in the "Edit Scale" pop-up window, click on the **Binning** tab, select **Midpoint**, select **Midpoint/Cutpoint positions**, and enter the class midpoint values that you prefer. Click **OK** and the graph will be modified to use your class midpoint values based on your preferred class limits. This second graph below was modified to use class midpoint values of 45, 65, 85, 105, 125, 145.

Histogram with Class Midpoints of 45, 65, 85, 105, 125, 145

2-3 Normal Quantile Plots

The textbook points out that *normal quantile plots* are helpful in determining whether sample data appear to be from a population having a normal distribution. Section 6-5 in the textbook discusses methods for *assessing normality*, and Section 2-3 in the textbook includes a brief discussion of normal quantile plots. Minitab generates Probability Plots that can be interpreted using the same criteria for normal quantile plots.

Minitab Procedure for a Probability Plot

1. Enter the data in a Minitab column, such as column C1. If the data are already stored in a Minitab worksheet, open the worksheet using the procedure described in Section 1-2 of this manual/workbook.

2. Click on the main menu item of **Graph**.

3. Select **Probability Plot** from the subdirectory.

4. Click on the option of **Single**, then click **OK**.

5. In the dialog box, identify the column to be used, then click **OK**.

Here is the probability plot obtained by using the full IQ scores listed in Section 2-1 of this manual/workbook.

2-4 Scatterplots

The textbook describes a scatterplot (or scatter diagram). A scatterplot can be very helpful in seeing a relationship between two variables. The scatterplot shown below results from paired data consisting of the number of chirps per minute by a cricket and the temperature. This scatterplot shows that as the number of chirps increases, the corresponding temperature tends to be higher.

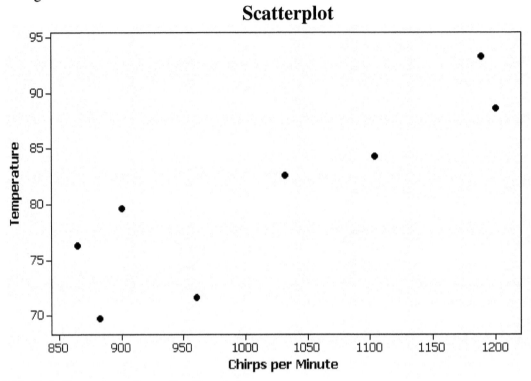

Minitab Procedure for a Scatterplot

1.   Given a collection of paired data, enter the values for one of the variables in column C1, and enter the corresponding values for the second variable in column C2. (You can also use any two Minitab columns other than C1 and C2.) Be careful to enter the two columns of data so that they are matched in the same way that they are paired in the original listing.

2.   Click on **Graph** from the main menu.

3.   Select the subdirectory item of **Scatterplot.** Select the option of **Simple**, then click **OK**.

4.   In the dialog box, enter C1 in the box for the Y variable, then enter C2 in the box for the X variable (or vice versa).

5.   Click **OK**.

A scatterplot can also be generated using **Stat**, then **Regression**, then **Fitted Line Plot**. We will use this option later in Chapter 10 when we discuss the topics of correlation and regression.

2-5 Time–Series Graph

Time–series data are data that have been collected at different points in time, and Minitab can graph such data so that patterns become easier to recognize.

Minitab Procedure for a Time–Series Graph

1. Given a collection of time–series data, enter the sequential values in a column, such as C1.

2. Select the main menu item of **Graph**.

3. Select the menu item of **Time Series Plot.**

4. Select the option of **Simple.**

5. A dialog box now appears. Enter the column label (such as C1) in the "Series" box.

6. Click **Time/Scale.**

7. Select the desired time scale (such as "Calendar"), and also select the appropriate interval (such as "Year").

8. Enter a start value (such as 1965) and a "Data Increment" value (such as 1).

9. Click **OK** twice.

Listed below are the high values of the Dow Jones Industrial Average (DJIA) for a sequence of recent and consecutive years. The time-series graph on the next page does a good job of showing the behavior of that stock market index.

969	995	943	985	969	842	951	1036	1052	892
882	1015	1000	908	898	1000	1024	1071	1287	1287
1553	1956	2722	2184	2791	3000	3169	3413	3794	3978
5216	6561	8259	9374	11568	11401	11350	10635	10454	10855
10941	12464	14198	13279	10580	11625	12929	13589	16577	18054

Time Series Plot of DJIA Annual High

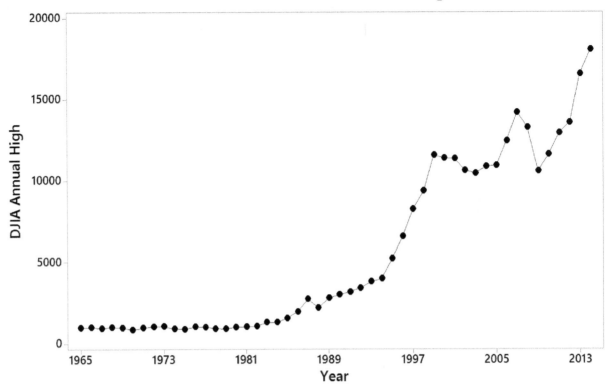

2-6 Dotplots

Minitab Procedure for a Dotplot

1.   Enter or retrieve the data into a Minitab column.

2.   Click on the main menu item of **Graph**.

3.   Select **Dotplot**.

4.   Select the **Simple** dotplot and click **OK**.

5.   The dialog box will list the columns of data at the left. Click on the desired column. You can edit a dotplot or any other graph by double-clicking on the attribute you want to modify. To change the scale, double-click on the axis and use the pop-up window.

6.   Click **OK**.

Shown below is the default Minitab dotplot display of the full IQ scores listed in Section 2-1 of this manual/workbook. The second dotplot was modified to show the more convenient values of 50, 60, 70, . . . , 150 along the horizontal scale. This change in the numbers used for the horizontal scale was made by double-clicking on a number on the horizontal scale, selecting the **scale** tab, then manually entering the values of 40, 50, 60, 70, . . . , 150 in the box labeled **Position of ticks**.

Default Dotplot

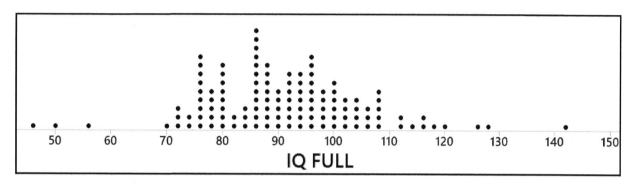

Dotplot With the Horizontal Scale Modified

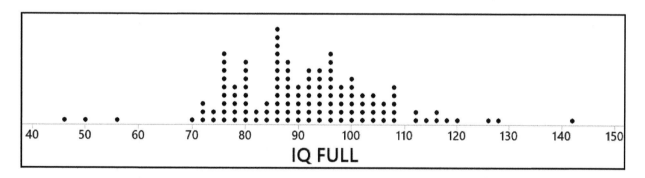

2-7 Stemplots

Minitab can provide stemplots (or stem-and-leaf plots). The textbook notes that a **stemplot** represents data by separating each value into two parts: the stem (such as the leftmost digit) and the leaf (such as the rightmost digit).

Minitab Procedure for a Stemplot

1.   Enter or retrieve the data into a Minitab column.

2.   Click on the main menu item of **Graph**.

3.   Select **Stem-and-Leaf**.

4.   The dialog box lists columns of data at the left. Click on the desired column.

5.   Remove the check mark for "Trim outliers," so that outliers will be included.

6.   Enter a desired value for the class interval, such as 10.

7.   Click **OK**.

Shown below is the Minitab stemplot based on the full IQ scores listed in the data set "IQ and Lead" in Appendix B of the textbook. The actual stemplot is highlighted below with a bold font. This stemplot is based on the use of 10 as the increment value.

Stem-and-Leaf Display: IQFULL

```
Stem-and-leaf of IQFULL   N  = 78
Leaf Unit = 1.0

    2     5    06
    2     6
   15     7    0234566666778
   35     8    00045555666677888999
  (21)    9    123444566666667789999
   22    10    01124455677778
    8    11    1558
    4    12    058
    1    13
    1    14    1
```

Reading and Interpreting a Minitab Stemplot: In addition to the stemplot itself, Minitab also provides another column of data at the extreme left as shown above. In the above display, *the leftmost column represents cumulative totals.* The left column above shows that there are 2 sample values included between 50 and 59. The left column entry of "(21)" indicates that there are 21 data values in the row containing the median. The left-column entries *below* the median row represent cumulative totals from the bottom up, so that the 1 at the bottom indicates that there is one value between 140 and 149. This leftmost column of values is tricky to interpret, so ignoring it would not be the worst thing that could be done in your life.

2-8 Bar Graphs

Shown below is a typical Minitab-generated bar graph. The procedure for generating such a bar graph is as follows.

1.   Enter the *names* of the categories (such as Jet Ski, Motorboat, and so on), in column C1.

2.   Enter the corresponding frequencies or percentage values in column C2.

3.   Click on **Graph**.

4.   Click on **Bar Chart.**

5.   In the "Bars represent" box at the top, select the option of **Values from a table**.

6.   Click on the **Simple** bar graph at the left, then click **OK**.

7.   In the "Graph variables" box, enter C2 (or whatever column contains the frequencies or percentage values).

8.   In the "Categorical variable" box, enter C1 (or whatever column contains the names of the categories).

9.   Click **OK**.

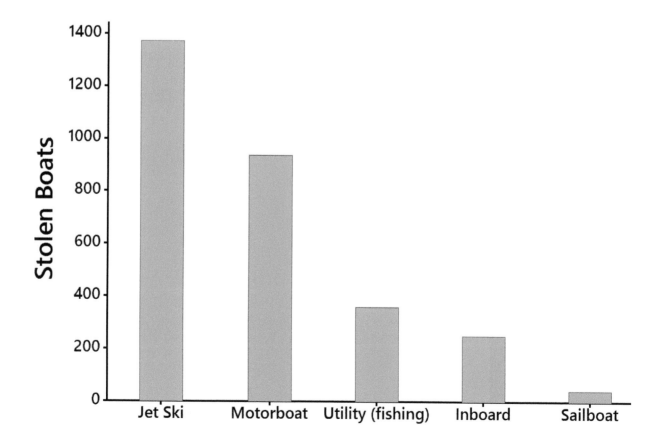

2-9 Pareto Charts

Section 2-3 of the textbook includes a description of Pareto charts. A Pareto chart is a bar graph for categorical data, with the bars arranged in order according to frequencies. The tallest bar is at the left, and the smaller bars are farther to the right. In the above bar chart, the bars are arranged in descending order, so this bar graph is a Pareto chart. Pareto charts can also be constructed by selecting **Stat**, **Quality Tools**, and **Pareto Chart**. The result may include more information than you really want, so it might be better to construct a Pareto chart by using the procedure in Section 2-9 for a bar chart, but arrange the table of data so that the frequencies are in descending order.

2-10 Pie Charts

To obtain a pie chart from Minitab, follow this procedure.

1. Enter the *names* of the categories in column C1.

2. Enter the corresponding frequency counts in column C2.

3. Select the main menu item of **Graph**.

4. Select **Pie Chart**.

5. When the dialog box is displayed, select **Chart values from a table** and enter C1 for the categorical variable box and enter C2 in the summary variables box.

6. Click **OK**. Shown on the next page is a Minitab pie chart describing boat-theft data.

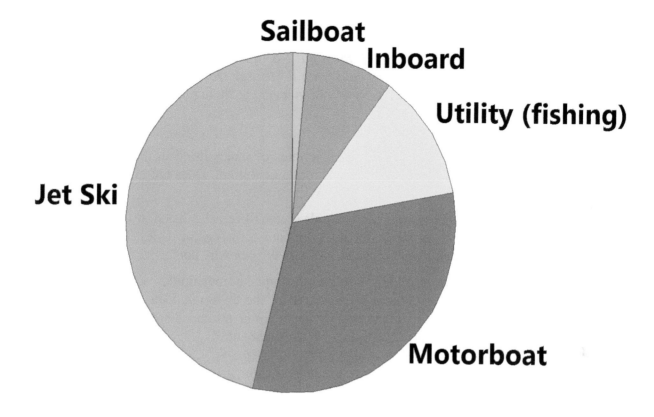

The textbook points out that the Pareto chart and the pie chart depict the same data in different ways, but the Pareto chart does a better job of showing the relative sizes of the different components. The textbook includes this suggestion from graphics expert Edwin Tufte:

> **Never use pie charts because they waste ink on components that are not data, and they lack an appropriate scale.**

CHAPTER 2 EXPERIMENTS: **Summarizing and Graphing Data**

Histograms. *In Experiments 2-1 through 2-6, use the data with Minitab to construct a histogram. Each experiment uses data from a Minitab worksheet corresponding to a data set in Appendix B of the textbook. It is not necessary to use a specific class width or class boundaries.*

2-1.   *Pulse Rates of Males* Use the pulse rates of males listed in the "Body Data" dataset in Appendix B of the textbook. Construct a histogram. Does the histogram appear to depict data having a normal distribution? Why or why not?

2-2.   *Pulse Rates of Females* Use the pulse rates of females listed in the "Body Data" dataset in Appendix B of the textbook. Construct a histogram. Does the histogram appear to depict data having a normal distribution? Why or why not?

2-3.   *Earthquake Magnitudes* Use the earthquake magnitudes listed in the "Earthquake Measurements" data set in Appendix B of the textbook. Construct a histogram. Using a loose interpretation of the requirements for a normal distribution, do the magnitudes appear to be normally distributed? Why or why not?

2-4.   *Earthquake Depths* Use the earthquake depths listed in the "Earthquake Measurements" data set in Appendix B of the textbook. Construct a histogram. Using a loose interpretation of the requirements for a normal distribution, do the depths appear to be normally distributed? Why or why not?

2-5.   *Male Red Blood Cell Counts* Use the red blood cell counts of males listed in the "Body Data" dataset in Appendix B of the textbook. Construct a histogram. Using a very loose interpretation of the requirements for a normal distribution, do the red blood cell counts appear to be normally distributed? Why or why not?

2-6.   *Female Red Blood Cell Counts* Use the red blood cell counts of females listed in the "Body Data" dataset in Appendix B of the textbook. Construct a histogram. Using a very loose interpretation of the requirements for a normal distribution, do the red blood cell counts appear to be normally distributed? Why or why not?

Scatterplots. *In Experiments 2-7 through 2-10, use the given paired data from Appendix B to construct a scatterplot. Each experiment uses data from a Minitab worksheet corresponding to a data set in Appendix B of the textbook.*

2-7.   *President's Heights* Refer to the "Presidents" dataset in Appendix B and use the heights of U. S. Presidents and the heights of their main opponents in the election campaign. Does there appear to be a correlation?

2-8.   *Brain Volume and IQ* Refer to the "IQ and Brain Size" dataset in Appendix B and use the brain volumes (cm^3) and IQ scores. A simple hypothesis is that people with larger brains are more intelligent and they have higher IQ scores. Does the scatterplot support that hypothesis?

2-9.   ***Bear Chest Size and Weight***   Refer to the "Bear Measurements" dataset in Appendix B and use the measured chest sizes and weights of bears. Does there appear to be a correlation between those two variables?

2-10.   ***Coke Volume and Weight***   Refer to the "Cola Weights and Volumes" data set in Appendix B and use the volumes and weights of regular Coke. Does there appear to be a correlation between volume and weight? What else is notable about the arrangement of the points, and how can it be explained?

Time Series Graphs.   *In Experiments 2-11 and 2-12, construct the time series graph.*

2-11.   ***Harry Potter***   Listed below are the gross amounts (in millions of dollars) earned from box office receipts for the movie *Harry Potter and the Half-Blood Prince*. The movie opened on a Wednesday, and the amounts are listed in order for the first 14 days of the movie's release. What is an explanation for the fact that the three highest amounts are the first, third, and fourth values listed?

58 22 27 29 21 10 10 8 7 9 11 9 4 4

2-12.   ***Law Enforcement Fatalities***   Listed below are the annual numbers of law enforcement fatalities in the United States for each year beginning with 1995 (listed in order by row). Is there a trend?

| 183 | 140 | 172 | 171 | 144 | 162 | 241 | 159 | 150 | 165 |
| 163 | 156 | 192 | 148 | 125 | 161 | 171 | 126 | 107 | 117 |

Dotplots.   *In Experiments 2-13 and 2-14, construct the dotplot.*

2-13.   ***Coke Volumes***   Refer to the "Cola Weights and Volumes" dataset in Appendix B and use the volumes of regular Coke. Does the configuration of the points appear to suggest that the volumes are from a population with a normal distribution? Why or why not? Are there any outliers?

2-14.   ***Car Pollution***   Refer to the "Car Measurements" dataset in Appendix B and use the greenhouse gas emissions (GHG) from the sample of cars. Does the configuration of the points appear to suggest that the amounts are from a population with a normal distribution? Why or why not?

Stemplots. In Experiments 2-15 and 2-16, refer to the data and use Minitab to construct a stemplot.

2-15. ***Car Crash Tests*** Refer to the "Car Crash Tests" dataset in Appendix B and use the 21 pelvis (PLVS) deceleration measurements from the car crash tests. Is there strong evidence suggesting that the data are *not* from a population having a normal distribution?

2-16. ***Car Braking Distances*** Refer to the "Car Measurements" dataset in Appendix B and use the 21 braking distances (ft). Are there any outliers? Is there strong evidence suggesting that the data are *not* from a population having a normal distribution?

Pareto Charts. *In Experiments 2-17 and 2-18, construct the Pareto chart.*

2-17. ***Awful Sounds*** In a survey, 1004 adults were asked to identify the most frustrating sound that they hear in a day. 279 chose jackhammers, 388 chose car alarms, 128 chose barking dogs, and 209 chose crying babies (based on data from Kelton Research).

2-18. ***School Day*** Here are weekly instruction times for school children in different countries: 23.8 hours (Japan); 26.9 hours (China); 22.2 hours (U.S.), 24.6 hours (U.K.); 24.8 hours (France). What do these results suggest about education in the United States?

Pie Charts. *In Experiments 2-19 and 2-20, construct the pie chart.*

2-19. ***Awful Sounds*** Use the data from Experiment 2-17.

2-20. ***School Day*** Use the data from Experiment 2-18. Does it make sense to use a pie chart for the given data?

2–21. ***Working with Your Own Data***   Through observation or experimentation, collect your own set of sample data values. Obtain at least 40 values and try to select data from an interesting population. Use Minitab to generate and print graphs suitable for describing the distribution of the data. Describe the data and any notable or important characteristics.

_____

_____

_____

_____

_____

3

Statistics for Describing, Exploring, and Comparing Data

Important note: The topics of this chapter require that you use Minitab to enter data, download worksheets of data, save worksheets, and print results. These functions are described in Chapter 1 of this manual/ workbook. Be sure to understand those functions from Chapter 1 before beginning this chapter.

The textbook notes that these characteristics of a data set are extremely important: center, variation, distribution, outliers, and changing characteristics of data over time. Chapter 2 of this manual/workbook presented a variety of graphs that are helpful in learning about the distribution of a data set. This chapter presents methods for learning about center, variation, and outliers.

3-1 Descriptive Statistics

Section 2-1 in this manual/workbook includes the following full IQ scores of subjects from the low lead group, included in the dataset "IQ and Lead" in Appendix B, and included in the Minitab worksheet named IQ and LEAD.MTW.

Full IQ Scores of Low Lead Group

```
 70 85 86  76  84 96  94 56 115  97  77 128  99  80 118 86 141 88  96 96
107 86 80 107 101 91 125 96  99  99 115 106 105  96  50 99  85 88 120 93
 87 98 78 100 105 87  94 89  80 111 104  85  94  75  73 76 107 88  89 96
 72 97 76 107 104 85  76 95  86  89  76  96 101 108 102 77  74 92
```

Given a data set, such as the above list of IQ scores, we can use Minitab to obtain descriptive statistics, including the mean, standard deviation, and quartiles.

Minitab Procedure for Descriptive Statistics

1.   Enter or open the data in a Minitab column, such as C1. (See Section 1-2.)

2.   Click on the main menu item of **Stat**.

3.   Click on the subdirectory item of **Basic Statistics**.

4.   Select **Display Descriptive Statistics**.

5.   A "Display Descriptive Statistics" dialog box will pop up. In the "Variables" box enter the column containing the data that you are investigating. You can manually enter the column, such as C1, or the name of the column, or you can click on the desired column displayed at the left.
   - You can also click on the **Graphs** bar to generate certain graphs, including a histogram and boxplot.
   - You can also click on the **Statistics** bar to select the particular statistics that you want included among the results.

6.   Click **OK**.

If you use the IQ scores listed on the preceding page and follow the above procedure, you will get a Minitab display like the one shown below. For this display, the author clicked on the **Statistics** bar and selected the statistics that are particularly relevant to discussions in the textbook.

```
Descriptive Statistics: IQFULL

             Total
Variable     Count    Mean  StDev  Variance  Minimum     Q1 Median      Q3
IQFULL          78   92.88  15.34    235.45    50.00  84.75  94.00  101.25


Variable  Maximum   Range
IQFULL     141.00   91.00
```

From the above Minitab display, we obtain the following important descriptive statistics (expressed by applying the round-off rule of using one more decimal place than in the original data values).

- Number of data values: 78
- Mean: $\bar{x} = 92.9$
- Standard deviation: $s = 15.3$
- Variance: $s^2 = 235.5$
- Range: 91.0
- Five-number-summary:
  - Minimum: 50
  - First quartile Q_1:   84.8
  - Median: 94.0
  - Third quartile Q_3:   101.3
  - Maximum: 141

Quartiles: The textbook uses a simplified procedure for finding quartiles, so the quartiles Q_1 and Q_3 found with Minitab may differ slightly from those found by using the procedure described in the textbook. For the above IQ scores, Minitab's quartiles of 84.8 and 101.3 differ slightly from the values of 85.0 and 101.0 that would be obtained by using the method described in the textbook.

3-2 *z* Scores

Section 3-3 in the textbook describes *z* scores (or standard scores). The *z* score can be found for a sample value *x* by computing one of the following:

Sample   **Population**

$$z = \frac{x - \bar{x}}{s} \quad \text{or} \quad z = \frac{x - \mu}{\sigma}$$

Here is the Minitab procedure for finding *z* scores corresponding to sample *x* values. (This procedure uses column C1, but any other Minitab column can be used instead.)

1. Enter a list of data values in column C1.

2. Click on the main menu item of **Calc**.

3. Select **Standardize** from the subdirectory.

4. The "Standard" dialog box will appear. Enter C1 for the input column and C2 (or any other specific column) for the column in which the *z*-score results will be stored.

5. There are buttons for different calculations, but be sure to select the top button for **"Subtract mean and divide by standard deviation."**

6. Click **OK**, and column C2 will magically appear with the *z* score equivalent of each of the original sample values. Because column C2 is now available as a set of data, you can explore it using Descriptive Statistics, Histogram, Dotplot, and so on.

Shown below are the first few rows from the Minitab display of the *z* scores for the list of full IQ scores of the low lead group listed in Section 3-1 of this manual/workbook. The column label of "*z* Score" was manually entered.

IQ FULL	Z Score
70	-1.49139
85	-0.51384
86	-0.44867
76	-1.10037
84	-0.57901

3-3 Boxplots

Section 3-3 in the textbook describes the construction of boxplots based on the minimum value, maximum value, median, and quartiles Q_1 and Q_3. Two important notes are relevant here:
- Minitab-generated boxplots are actually *modified boxplots* as described in Part 2 of Section 3-3.
- The values of Q_1 and Q_3 generated by Minitab may be slightly different from the values obtained by using the procedure described in the textbook.

Minitab Procedure for Boxplots

1.   Enter the data or open a worksheet with data.

2.   Click on the main menu item of **Graph**.

3.   Select the subdirectory item of **Boxplot**.

4.   Select **One Y Simple** for one boxplot or select **Multiple Y's Simple** for boxplots of two or more data sets.

5.   In the dialog box, click on the column(s) containing the data for which the boxplot will be produced.

6.   Click **OK**.

Shown below are the two boxplots for the pulse rates of females and males listed in the "Body Data" dataset from Appendix B in the textbook. Boxplots are particularly useful for comparing data sets. The asterisks are used to identify data values that appear to be outliers. By comparing the two boxplots, we see that the pulse rates of females appear to be a little higher than those of males.

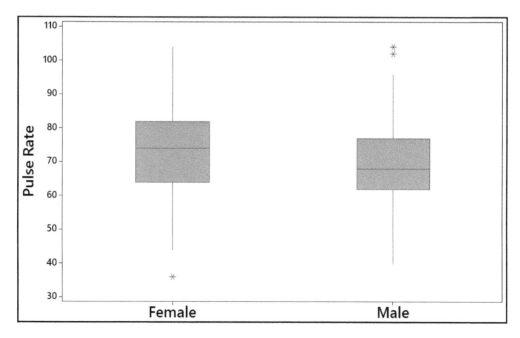

3-4 Outliers

Minitab does not have a specific function for identifying outliers, but some of the functions described in this chapter can be used. One easy procedure for identifying outliers is to *sort* the data as described in Section 1-6 of this manual/workbook, then simply examine the values near the beginning of the list or the end of the list. Consider a value to be an outlier if it is very far away from almost all of the other data values.

Another way to identify outliers is to construct a boxplot. We have noted that Minitab uses asterisks to depict outliers that are identified with a specific criterion that uses the *interquartile range* (IQR). The interquartile range IQR is as follows:

$$IQR = Q_3 - Q_1$$

Minitab identifies data values as outliers and denotes them with asterisks in a boxplot by applying these same criteria given in Part 2 of Section 3-3 from the textbook:

A data value is an outlier if it is …

above Q_3 by an amount greater than $1.5 \times IQR$
or   below Q_1 by an amount greater than $1.5 \times IQR$

For example, see the boxplots given in Section 3-3 of this manual/workbook and note that the pulse rates of females are depicted with a boxplot that includes one asterisk corresponding to the lowest pulse rate of 36 beats per minute. When analyzing these pulse rates of females, it is a good strategy to consider the effect of that value by considering results with that value included and the results obtained when that value is excluded.

Remember that important characteristics of data sets are center, variation, distribution, outliers, and time (that is, changing characteristics of data over time). Outliers are important for a variety of reasons. Some outliers are errors that should be corrected. Some outliers are correct values that may have a very dramatic effect on results and conclusions, so it is important to know when outliers are present so that their effects can be considered.

CHAPTER 3 EXPERIMENTS:
Statistics for Describing, Exploring, and Comparing Data

3–1. ***Comparing Heights of Males and Females*** In this experiment we use two small data sets as a quick introduction to using some of the basic Minitab features. (When beginning work with new software, it is wise to first work with small data sets so that they can be entered quickly if they are lost or damaged.) The data listed below are measured heights (cm) of random samples of men and women .

Male	178.8	177.5	187.8	172.4	181.7	169.0
Female	163.7	165.5	163.1	166.3	163.6	170.9

a. Find the indicated characteristics of the heights of *males* and enter the results below.

Center: Mean: _____   Median: _____

Variation: St. Dev.:_____   Range: _____

5-Number Summary: Min.:_____ Q_1:_____ Q_2:_____ Q_3:_____ Max.:_____

Outliers: _____

b. Find the characteristics of the heights of *females* and enter the results below.

Center: Mean: _____   Median: _____

Variation: St. Dev.:_____   Range: _____

5-Number Summary: Min.:_____ Q_1:_____ Q_2:_____ Q_3:_____ Max.:_____

Outliers: _____

c. Compare the results from parts (a) and (b).

_____

_____

_____

3–2.   ***Working with Larger Data Sets*** Repeat Experiment 3–1, but use the sample data for all 300 subjects included in the "Body Data" dataset that is found in Appendix B of the textbook. That data set can be downloaded at www.TriolaStats.com as described in Section 1-2 of this manual/workbook. *Hint:* Because the data for males and females are used separately, *unstack* the heights based on gender, as described in Section 1-6 of this manual/workbook.

a. Find the indicated characteristics of the heights of *males* and enter the results below.

Center: Mean: _____   Median: _____

Variation: St. Dev.:_____   Range: _____

5-Number Summary: Min.:_____ Q_1:_____ Q_2:_____ Q_3:_____ Max.:_____

Outliers: _____

b. Find the characteristics of the heights of *females* and enter the results below.

Center: Mean: _____   Median: _____

Variation: St. Dev.:_____   Range: _____

5-Number Summary: Min.:_____ Q_1:_____ Q_2:_____ Q_3:_____ Max.:_____

Outliers: _____

c. Compare the results from parts a and b.

_____

_____

_____

d. Are there are notable differences observed from the complete sets of sample data that could not be seen with the smaller samples listed in Experiment 3–1? If so, what are they?

_____

_____

_____

3–3. **_Boxplots_** Use the same sets of data used in Experiment 3–2 and print boxplots for the heights of the males and the heights of the females. Include both boxplots in the same window so that they can be compared. Do the boxplots suggest any notable differences in the two sets of sample data?

_____

_____

Interpret the *asterisk* that appears in the Minitab display for the boxplot depicting the heights of the females. Identify the value that this asterisk represents.

_____

_____

3–4. **_Effect of Outlier_** In this experiment we will study the effect of an *outlier*. Use the same heights of *men* used in Experiment 3-1, but change the first entry from 178.8 cm. to 1788 cm. (This type of mistake often occurs when the key for the decimal point is not pressed with enough force.) The outlier of 1788 cm is clearly a mistake, because a male with of height of 1788 cm would be 59 feet tall, or about six stories tall. Although this outlier is a mistake, outliers are sometimes correct values that differ substantially from the other sample values.

Males (cm): **1788** 177.5 187.8 172.4 181.7 169.0

Using this modified data set with the height of 178.8 cm changed to be the outlier of 1788 cm, find the following.

Center:　　Mean: _____　　Median: _____

Variation:　St. Dev.:_____　　Range: _____

5-Number Summary: Min.:_____ Q_1:_____ Q_2:_____ Q_3:_____ Max.:_____

Outliers: _____

Based on a comparison of these results to those found in Experiment 3–1, how is the mean affected by the presence of an outlier?

_____

How is the median affected by the presence of an outlier?

_____

How is the standard deviation affected by the presence of an outlier?

_____

3–5.   ***Describing Data*** Use the BMI (body mass index) indices of *females* from the "Body Data" dataset in Appendix B from the textbook, and enter the results indicated below. (The Minitab worksheet is Body Data.MTW.) *Hint:* Because the data for males and females are used separately in this project and the following project, *unstack* the BMI values based on gender, as described in Section 2-2 of this manual/workbook.

   Center: Mean: _____   Median: _____

   Variation: St. Dev.:_____   Range: _____

   5-Number Summary: Min.:_____ Q_1:_____ Q_2:_____ Q_3:_____ Max.:_____

   Outliers: _____

3–6.   ***Describing Data*** Use the BMI (body mass index) indices of *males* from the "Body Data" dataset in Appendix B from the textbook, and enter the results indicated below. (The Minitab worksheet is Body Data.MTW.)

   Center: Mean: _____   Median: _____

   Variation: St. Dev.:_____   Range: _____

   5-Number Summary: Min.:_____ Q_1:_____ Q_2:_____ Q_3:_____ Max.:_____

   Outliers: _____

   Compare the BMI indices of females (from Experiment 3-5) and males.

   _____

   _____

3–7.   ***Boxplots*** Use the BMI indices of females (see Experiment 3-5) and use the BMI indices of males (see Experiment 3-6). Print their two boxplots together in the same display. Do the boxplots suggest any notable differences in the two sets of sample data?

   _____

   _____

3–8.   ***Sorting Data*** Use the earthquake magnitudes listed in the "Earthquakes" dataset from Appendix B in the textbook. (The Minitab worksheet is Earthquakes.MTW.) *Sort* that data set by arranging the magnitudes from lowest to highest. In the space below, list the first ten values in the sorted column.

   _____

3–9.   *z Scores*   Open the Minitab worksheet "Aluminum Cans.MTW," then use Minitab to find the *z* score corresponding to each of the 175 values for the cans that are 0.0109 in. thick. [Each value is an axial load, which is the weight (in pounds) that the can supports before being crushed.] Store the 175 *z* scores in column C3, then use column C3 to find the following.

     Center: Mean: _____   Median: _____

     Variation: St. Dev.:_____   Range: _____

     5-Number Summary: Min.:_____ Q_1:_____ Q_2:_____ Q_3:_____   Max.:_____

     Outliers: _____

What is notable about the above results? Specifically, what is notable about the value of the mean and standard deviation?

_____

Will the same mean and standard deviation be obtained for *any* set of sample data? Explain how you arrived at your answer.

_____

_____

3–10.   *Combining Data*   Open the Minitab worksheet "M&M Weights", which consists of six different columns of data. Use **Data/Stack** to make a copy of the data all stacked together in column C7 of the current worksheet.

     a. Find the following results for the combined data in column C7.

         Center: Mean: _____   Median: _____

         Variation: St. Dev.:_____   Range: _____

         5-Number Summary: Min.:_____ Q_1:_____ Q_2:_____ Q_3:_____   Max.:_____

         Outliers: _____

     b. Print a boxplot of the data set.

     c. Describe the important characteristics of the data set. Be sure to address the nature of the distribution, measures of center, measures of variation, and any other important and notable features.

_____

_____

3–11. ***Statistics from a Dotplot*** Shown below is a Minitab dotplot. Identify the values represented in this graph, enter them in column C1, then find the indicated results.

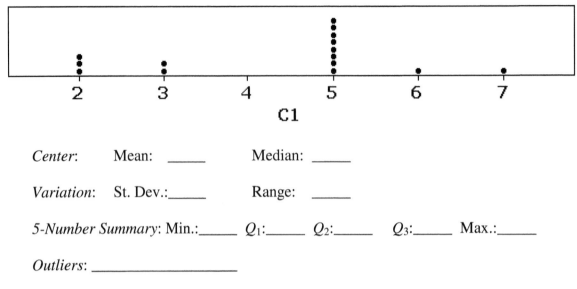

Center: Mean: _____   Median: _____

Variation: St. Dev.:_____   Range: _____

5-Number Summary: Min.:_____ Q_1:_____ Q_2:_____ Q_3:_____ Max.:_____

Outliers: _____

3–12. ***Comparing Data*** Open the Minitab worksheet "Cola Weights and Volumes" and use Minitab to compare the weights of regular Coke and the weights of diet Coke. Obtain printouts of relevant results. What do you conclude? Can you explain any substantial difference?

_____

_____

3–13. ***Comparing Data*** In "Tobacco and Alcohol Use in G–Rated Children's Animated Films," by Goldstein, Sobel and Newman (*Journal of the American Medical Association*, Vol. 281, No. 12), the lengths (in seconds) of scenes showing tobacco use and alcohol use were recorded for animated children's movies. Refer to the "Alcohol and Tobacco in Movies" data set in Appendix B from the textbook. Find the mean and median for the tobacco times, then find the mean and median for the alcohol times. Does there appear to be a difference between those times? Which appears to be the larger problem: scenes showing tobacco use or scenes showing alcohol use?

_____

_____

_____

_____

3–14. ***Working with Your Own Data*** Through observation or experimentation, collect your own set of sample values. Obtain at least 40 values and try to select data from an interesting population. List the values below.

_____

_____

_____

_____

_____

_____

_____

_____

Find the following results.

Center: Mean: _____   Median: _____

Variation: St. Dev.:_____   Range: _____

5-Number Summary: Min.:_____ Q_1:_____ Q_2:_____ Q_3:_____ Max.:_____

Outliers: _____

Use Minitab to further explore the data. Obtain printouts of relevant results. Describe the nature of the data. That is, what do the values represent? Describe important characteristics of the data set, and include Minitab printouts to support your observations.

4

Probabilities Through Simulations

4-1 Simulation Methods

Chapter 4 in the Triola textbook focuses on principles of probability theory. That chapter presents a variety of rules and methods for finding probabilities of different events. The textbook focuses on traditional approaches to computing probability values, but this chapter in this manual/workbook focuses instead on an alternative approach based on *simulations*.

> A **simulation** of a procedure is a process that behaves the same way as the procedure, so that similar results are produced.

Mathematician Stanislaw Ulam once studied the problem of finding the probability of winning a game of solitaire, but the theoretical computations involved were too complicated. Instead, Ulam took the approach of programming a computer to simulate or "play" solitaire hundreds of times. The ratio of wins to total games played is the approximate probability he sought. This same type of reasoning was used to solve important problems that arose during World War II. There was a need to determine how far neutrons would penetrate different materials, and the method of solution required that the computer make various random selections in much the same way that it can randomly select the outcome of the rolling of a pair of dice. This neutron diffusion project was named the Monte Carlo Project and we now refer to general methods of simulating experiments as *Monte Carlo methods*. Such methods are the focus of this chapter. The concept of simulation is quite easy to understand with simple examples.

- We could simulate the rolling of a die by using Minitab to randomly generate whole numbers between 1 and 6 inclusive, provided that the computer selects from the numbers 1, 2, 3, 4, 5, and 6 in such a way that those outcomes are equally likely.

- We could simulate births by flipping a coin, where "heads" represents a baby girl and "tails" represents a baby boy. We could also simulate births by using Minitab to randomly generate 0s (for baby girls) and 1s (for baby boys).

It is extremely important to construct a simulation so that it behaves just like the real procedure. The following example illustrates a right way and a wrong way.

EXAMPLE   Describe a procedure for simulating the rolling of a *pair* of dice.
SOLUTION   In the procedure of rolling a pair of dice, each of the two dice yields a number between 1 and 6 (inclusive) and those two numbers are then added. Any simulation should do exactly the same thing.

> ***Right way*** to simulate rolling two dice: Randomly generate one number between 1 and 6, then randomly generate another number between 1 and 6, then add the two results.
>
> ***Wrong way*** to simulate rolling two dice: Randomly generate numbers between 2 and 12. This procedure is similar to rolling dice in the sense that the results are always between 2 and 12, but these outcomes between 2 and 12 are equally likely. With real dice, the values between 2 and 12 are *not* equally likely. This simulation would yield terrible results.

4-2   Minitab Simulation Tools

Minitab includes several different tools that can be used for simulations.

1.   Click on the main menu item of **Calc**.

2.   Click on the subdirectory item of **Random Data**.

You will get a long list of different options, but we will use four of them (integer, uniform, Bernoulli, normal) that are particularly useful.

- **Integer:** Generates a sample of randomly selected integers with a specified minimum and maximum. This Minitab tool is particularly good for a variety of different simulations. Shown below is the dialog box that is provided when you select **Calc/Random Data/ Integer**. The entries in this box tell Minitab to randomly generate 5000 values between 1 and 6 inclusive, and put them in column C1. This simulates rolling a single die 5000 times.

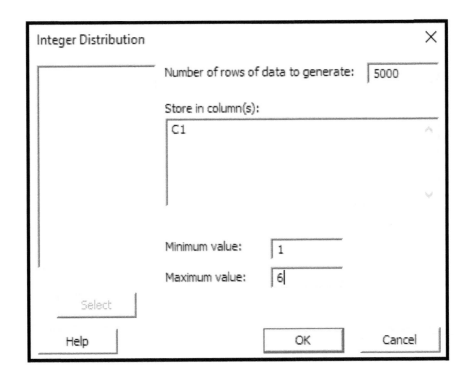

- **Uniform:** Select **Calc**, then **Random Data**, then **Uniform.** The generated values are "uniform" in the sense that all possible values have the same chance of being selected. The Minitab dialog box shown below has entries indicating that 5000 values should be randomly selected between 0.0 and 9.0. If you want whole numbers, use the Integer distribution instead of the Uniform distribution.

- **Bernoulli:** Select **Calc**, then **Random Data**, then **Bernoulli.** The dialog box below has entries that result in a column of 0s (failure) and 1s (success), where the probability of success is 0.5. This simulates flipping a coin 5000 times. The entries can be changed for different circumstances.

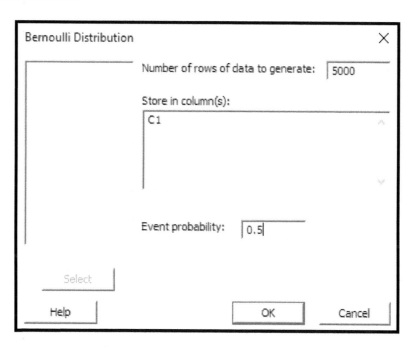

- **Normal:** Select **Calc**, then **Random Data**, then **Normal** to generate a sample of data randomly selected from a population having a normal distribution. (Normal distributions are discussed in Chapter 6 of the Triola textbook. For now, think of a normal distribution as one with a histogram that is bell–shaped.) You must enter the population mean and standard deviation. The entries in the dialog box below result in a simulated sample of 5000 IQ scores taken from a population with a bell-shaped distribution that has a mean of 100 and a standard deviation of 15. Shown below the dialog box is a Minitab-generated histogram displaying the bell-shaped nature of the generated data.

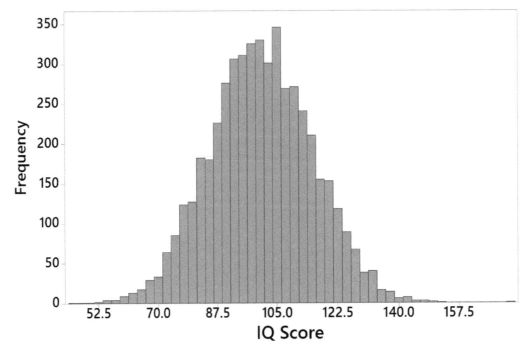

4-3   Simulation Examples

We will now illustrate the preceding Minitab features by describing specific simulations.

Simulation 1: Generating 50 births (boys/girls)

To simulate 50 births with the assumption that boys and girls are equally likely, use either of the following:

- Use Minitab's **Integer** distribution (see Section 4-2 of this manual/workbook) to generate 50 integers between 0 and 1. If you arrange the results in order (using the **Sort** feature as described in Section 1-6 of this manual/workbook), it is very easy to count the number of 0s (or boys) and the number of 1s (or girls).

- Use Minitab's **Bernoulli** distribution. Enter 50 for the sample size and enter 0.5 for the probability. Again, it is very easy to count the number of 1s (or boys) and the number of 0s (or girls) if the data are sorted, as described in Section 3-4 of this manual/workbook.

Simulation 2: Rolling a *single* die 60 times

To simulate 60 rolls of a single die, use Minitab's **Integer** distribution to generate 60 integers between 1 and 6. Again, sorting the generated values makes it easy to count the number of 1s, 2s, and so on.

Simulation 3: Rolling a *pair* of dice 750 times

To simulate the rolling of a *pair* of dice 750 times, use column C1 for one die, use column C2 for the second die, then let column C3 be the *sum* of columns C1 and C2. That is, create column C1 by using the method described in Simulation 2 above. Then create column C2 by again using the method described in Simulation 2 above. Then use **Calc/Calculator** to enter the expression C1 + C2 with the result stored in column C3.

Simulation 4: Generating 25 birth dates

Instead of generating 25 results such as "March 5," or "November 27," randomly generate 25 integers between 1 and 365 inclusive. (We are ignoring leap years). Use Minitab's **Integer** distribution and enter 25 for the sample size. Also enter 1 for the minimum and enter 365 for the maximum. If you sort the simulated birth dates by using the procedure in Section 1-6 of this manual/workbook, it becomes easy to scan the sorted list and determine whether there are two birth dates that are the same. If there are two birth dates that are the same, they will show up as *consecutive* equal values in the sorted list.

CHAPTER 4 EXPERIMENTS: Probabilities Through Simulations

4—1.   ***Birth Simulation***   Use Minitab to simulate 5000 births, where each birth results in a boy or girl. Sort the results, count the number of girls, and enter that value here:_____

Based on that result, estimate the probability of getting a girl when a baby is born. Enter the estimated probability here: _____

The preceding estimated probability is likely to be different from 0.5. Does this suggest that the computer's random number generator is defective? Why or why not?

_____

_____

4—2.   ***Dice Simulation***   Use Minitab to simulate 5000 rolls of a *pair* of dice. Sort the results, then find the number of times that the total was exactly 7. Enter that value here:_____

Based on that result, estimate the probability of getting a 7 when two dice are rolled. Enter the estimated probability here:_____

How does this estimated probability compare to the computed (theoretical) probability of 1/6 or 0.167? _____

_____

4—3.   ***Probability of at Least 11 Girls***
     a.   Use Minitab to simulate 20 births. Does the result consist of at least 11 girls? _____
     b.   Repeat part (a) nine more times and record the result from part (a) along with the other nine results here: ___ ___ ___ ___ ___ ___ ___ ___ ___ ___
     c.   Based on the results from part (b), what is the estimated probability of getting at least 11 girls in 20 births? _____

4-4.   ***Brand Recognition***   The probability of randomly selecting an adult who recognizes the brand name of McDonald's is 0.95 (based on data from Franchise Advantage). Use Minitab to develop a simulation so that each individual outcome should be an indication of one of two results: (1) The consumer recognizes the brand name of McDonald's; (2) the consumer does not recognize the brand name of McDonald's. (*Hint:* Randomly generate integers between 1 and 100, and consider results from 1 through 95 to be people who recognize the brand name of McDonald's.) Conduct the simulation 1000 times and record the number of consumers who recognize the brand name of McDonald's. Obtain a printed copy of the results. Is the proportion of those who recognize McDonald's reasonably close to the value of 0.95?

_____

_____

4-5. ***Simulating Hybridization*** When Mendel conducted his famous hybridization experiments, he used peas with green pods and yellow pods. One experiment involved crossing peas in such a way that 75% of the offspring peas were expected to have green pods, and 25% of the offspring peas were expected to have yellow pods. Use Minitab to simulate 5000 peas in such a hybridization experiment. Each of the 5000 individual outcomes should be an indication of one of two results: (1) The pod is green; (2) the pod is yellow. Is the percentage of yellow peas from the simulation reasonably close to the value of 25%?

4—6. ***Probability of at Least 55 Girls*** Use Minitab to conduct a simulation for estimating the probability of getting at least 55 girls in 100 births. Enter the estimated probability here:_____ Describe the procedure used to obtain the estimated probability.

In testing a gender-selection method, assume that the Biogene Technology Corporation conducted an experiment with 100 couples who were treated, and that the 100 births included at least 55 girls. What should you conclude about the effectiveness of the treatment?

4—7. ***Probability of at Least 65 Girls*** Use Minitab to conduct a simulation for estimating the probability of getting at least 65 girls in 100 births. Enter the estimated probability here:_____
Describe the procedure used to obtain the estimated probability.

In testing a gender-selection method, if the Biogene Technology Corporation conducted an experiment with 100 couples who were treated, and the 100 births included at least 65 girls, what should you conclude about the effectiveness of the treatment?

4-8. ***Gender-Selection Method*** Results available from the Microsort YSORT method of gender-selection consist of 127 boys in 152 births. That is, among 152 sets of parents using the YSORT method for increasing the likelihood of a boy, 127 actually had boys and the other 25 had girls. Assuming that the YSORT method has no effect and that boys and girls are equally likely, use Minitab to simulate 152 births. Is 127 boys in 152 births a significantly high number of boys? What does the result suggest about the YSORT method?

4–9.   ***Simulating Three Dice*** Develop a simulation for rolling three dice. Simulate the rolling of the three dice 5000 times. Describe the simulation, then use it to estimate the probability of getting a total of 10 when three dice are rolled.

_____

_____

4–10.   ***Simulating Left–Handedness*** Assume that ten percent of us are left-handed. In a study of dexterity, people are randomly selected in groups of five. Develop a simulation for finding the probability of getting at least one left-handed person in a group of five. Simulate 100 groups of five. How does the probability compare to the correct result of 0.410, which can be found by using the probability rules in the textbook?

_____

_____

4–11.   ***Nasonex Treatment*** Nasonex is a nasal spray used to treat allergies. In clinical trials, 1671 subjects were given a placebo, and 2 of them developed upper respiratory tract infections. Another 2103 patients were treated with Nasonex and 6 of them developed upper respiratory tract infections. Assume that Nasonex has no effect on upper respiratory tract infections, so that the rate of those infections also applies to Nasonex users. Using the placebo rate of 2/1671, simulate groups of 2103 subjects given the Nasonex treatment, then determine whether a result of 6 upper respiratory tract infections could easily occur. Describe the results. What do the results suggest about Nasonex as a cause of upper respiratory tract infections?

_____

_____

4–12.   ***Birthdays*** Simulate a class of 25 birth dates by randomly generating 25 integers between 1 and 365. (Ignore leap years.) Arrange the birth dates in ascending order, then examine the list to determine whether at least two birth dates are the same. (This is easy to do, because any two equal integers must be next to each other.)

Generated "birth dates:"   __ __ __ __ __ __ __ __ __ __ __ __ __

                                __ __ __ __ __ __ __ __ __ __ __ __

Are at least two of the "birth dates" the same? _____

4—13. *Birthdays* Repeat the preceding experiment nine additional times and record all ten of the yes/no responses here:

____ ____ ____ ____ ____ ____ ____ ____ ____

Based on these results, what is the probability of getting at least two birth dates that are the same (when a class of 25 students is randomly selected)? _____

4—14. *Birthdays* Repeat Experiments 4-12 and 4-13 for 50 people instead of 25. Based on the results, what is the estimated probability of getting at least two birth dates that are the same (when a class of 50 students is randomly selected)? _____

4—15. *Birthdays* Repeat Experiments 4-12 and 4-13 for 100 people instead of 25. Based on the results, what is the estimated probability of getting at least two birth dates that are the same (when a class of 100 students is randomly selected)? _____

4—16. *Normally Distributed IQ Scores* IQ scores are normally distributed with a mean of 100 and a standard deviation of 15. Generate a normally distributed sample of 800 IQ scores by using the given mean and standard deviation. Sort the results (arrange them in ascending order).

   a. Examine the sorted results to estimate the probability of randomly selecting someone with an IQ score between 90 and 110 inclusive. Enter the result here._____
   b. Examine the sorted results to estimate the probability of randomly selecting someone with an IQ score greater than 115. _____
   c. Examine the sorted results to estimate the probability of randomly selecting someone with an IQ score less than 120. _____
   d. Repeat part (a) of this experiment nine more times and list all ten probabilities here.

   _____ _____ _____ _____ _____ _____ _____ _____ _____ _____

   e. Examine the ten probabilities obtained above and comment on the *consistency* of the results.

   _____

   f. How might we modify this experiment so that the results can become more consistent?

   _____

   g. If the results appear to be very consistent, what does that imply about any individual sample result?

   _____

4—17. ***Law of Large Numbers*** In this experiment we test the Law of Large Numbers, which states that "as an experiment is repeated again and again, the empirical probability of success tends to approach the actual probability." We will use a simulation of a single die, and we will consider a success to be the outcome of 1. (Based on the classical definition of probability, we know that $P(1) = 1/6 = 0.167$.)

   a. Simulate 5 trials by generating 5 integers between 1 and 6. Count the number of 6s that occurred and divide that number by 5 to get the empirical probability.
       Based on 5 trials, $P(1) =$ _____.

   b. Repeat part (a) for 25 trials. Based on 25 trials, $P(1)=$ _____.

   c. Repeat part (a) for 50 trials. Based on 50 trials, $P(1)=$ _____.

   d. Repeat part (a) for 500 trials. Based on 500 trials, $P(1)=$ _____.

   e. Repeat part (a) for 1000 trials. Based on 1000 trials, $P(1) =$ _____.

   f. In your own words, generalize these results in a restatement of the Law of Large Numbers.

   _____

   _____

   _____

   _____

4-18. ***Detecting Fabricated Results*** Consider a class experiment in which some students actually flip a coin 200 times and record the results, while others make up their own results for 200 coin flips. It is easy to identify the fabricated results using this criterion: If there is a run of six heads or six tails, the results are real, but if there is no such run, the results are fabricated. This is based on the principle that when fabricating results, people almost never include a run of six or more heads or tails, but with 200 actual coin flips, there is a very high probability of getting such a run of at least six heads or tails. The calculation for the probability of getting a run of at least six heads or six tails is *extremely* difficult, so conduct simulations to estimate that probability. Describe the process and identify the estimated probability that when 200 coins are tossed, there is run of at least six heads or tails.

   _____

   _____

   _____

   _____

4—19. ***Sticky Probability Problem*** Consider the following exercise, which is extremely difficult to solve with the formal rules of probability.

Two points along a straight stick are randomly selected. The stick is then broken at these two points. Find the probability that the three pieces can be arranged to form a triangle.

Instead of attempting a solution using formal rules of probability, we will use a simulation. The length of the stick is irrelevant, so assume it's one unit long and its length is measured from 0 at one end to 1 at the other end. Use Minitab to randomly select the two break points with the random generation of two numbers from a uniform distribution with a minimum of 0, a maximum of 1, and 4 decimal places. Plot the break points on the "stick" below.

0_____1

A triangle can be formed if the longest segment is less than 0.5, so enter the lengths of the three pieces here: _____   _____   _____

Can a triangle be formed?

Now repeat this process nine more times and summarize all of the results below.

Trial	Break Points		Triangle formed?
1			
2			
3			
4			
5			
6			
7			
8			
9			
10			

Based on the ten trials, what is the estimated probability that a triangle can be formed? _____ This estimate gets better with more trials.

5

Probability Distributions

5-1 Exploring Probability Distributions

Chapter 5 in the Triola textbook discusses probability distributions, and its focus is *discrete* probability distributions only. These important definitions are introduced:

Definitions

A **random variable** is a variable (typically represented by *x*) that has a single numerical value, determined by chance, for each outcome of a procedure.

A **probability distribution** is a description that gives the probability for each value of the random variable. It is often expressed in the format of a table, formula, or graph.

When working with a probability distribution, we should consider the same important characteristics introduced in Chapter 2:

1. **Center:** Measure of center, which is a representative or average value that gives us an indication of where the middle of the data set is located

2. **Variation:** A measure of the amount that the values vary among themselves

3. **Distribution:** The nature or shape of the distribution of the data, such as bell-shaped, uniform, or skewed

4. **Outliers:** Sample values that are very far away from the vast majority of the other sample values

5. **Time:** Changing characteristics of the data over time

Section 5-1 of this manual/workbook addresses these important characteristics for probability distributions. The characteristics of center and variation are addressed with formulas for finding the mean, standard deviation, and variance of a probability distribution. The characteristic of distribution is addressed through the graph of a probability histogram.

Although Minitab is not designed to deal directly with a probability distribution, it can often be used. Consider the probability distribution given in the accompanying table. This table lists the probabilities for the number girls in 2 births.

Number of Girls in 2 Births

x	*P(x)*
0	0.25
1	0.50
2	0.25

If you examine the data in the table, you can verify that a probability distribution is defined because the three key requirements are satisfied:

1. The variable x is a numerical random variable and its values are associated with probabilities, as in the table on the preceding page.
2. The sum of the probabilities is 1, as required. $(0.25 + 0.50 + 0.25 = 1.)$
3. Each value of $P(x)$ is between 0 and 1. (Specifically, 0.25 and 0.50 and 0.25 are each between 0 and 1 inclusive.)

Having determined that the table does define a probability distribution, let's now use Minitab to find the mean μ and standard deviation σ. Minitab is not designed to directly calculate the value of the mean and standard deviation, but there is a way to get those values, although it is not easy.

Minitab Procedure for Finding μ and σ for a Probability Distribution

1. Enter the values of the random variable x in column C1.

2. Enter the corresponding probabilities in column C2.

3. Calculate the mean μ by using Formula 5-1 in the textbook for the mean of a probability distribution: $\mu = \sum[x \cdot P(x)]$. This is accomplished by clicking on **Calc**, selecting **Calculator**, and entering the expression sum(C1*C2) with the result stored in column C3, as shown in the following screen.

4.   Now proceed to calculate the value of the standard deviation σ by using Formula 5-4 from the textbook: $\sigma = \sqrt{\left[\Sigma x^2 \cdot P(x)\right] - \mu^2}$. This is accomplished by selecting **Calc**, then **Calculator**, and entering the expression

$$\text{sqrt(sum(C1**2*C2)} - \text{C3**2)}$$

with the result stored in column C4.

If you use the above procedure with the table near the beginning of this section, the result will be as shown below. We can see that $\mu = 1$ and the standard deviation is $\sigma = 0.707107$ (or 0.7 after rounding). The names of the columns in the display below were manually entered.

x	P(x)	Mean	St. Dev.
0	0.25	1	0.707107
1	0.50		
2	0.25		

5-2 Binomial Distributions

A **binomial distribution** is defined in Section 5-2 of the Triola textbook to be to be a probability distribution that meets all of the following requirements:

1.   The procedure must have a fixed number of trials.
2.   The trials must be independent. (The outcome of any individual trial doesn't affect the probabilities in the other trials.)
3.   Each trial must have all outcomes classified into two categories.
4.   The probabilities must remain constant for each trial.

We also introduced notation with S and F denoting success and failure for the two possible categories of all outcomes. Also, p and q denote the probabilities of S and F, respectively, so that $P(S) = p$ and $P(F) = q$. We also use the following notation.

Notation

n = the fixed number of trials

x = specific number of successes in n trials so that x can be any whole number between 0 and n, inclusive

p = probability of success in *one* of the n trials

q = probability of failure in *one* of the n trials

$P(x)$ = probability of getting exactly x successes among the n trials

Section 5-2 in the Triola textbook describes three methods for determining probabilities in binomial experiments. Method 1 uses the binomial probability formula:

$$P(x) = \frac{n!}{(n-x)!x!} p^x q^{n-x}$$

Method 2 requires computer usage. We noted in the textbook that if a computer and software are available, this method of finding binomial probabilities is fast and easy, as shown in the Minitab procedure that follows. We illustrate the Minitab procedure with the following problem:

EXAMPLE   *Devil of a Problem* Based on a Harris poll, 60% of adults believe in the devil. Assuming that we randomly select 5 adults, find the probability that exactly 3 of the 5 adults believe in the devil

---

For this example, $n = 5$, $p = 0.60$, and the possible values of x are 0, 1, 2, 3, 4, 5.

Minitab Procedure for Finding Probabilities with a Binomial Distribution

1.   In column C1, enter the values of the random variable x for which you want probabilities. (You can enter all values of x as 0, 1, 2, . . .) Here are the entries for the x values of 0, 1, 2, 3, 4, 5:

2.   Click on **Calc** from the main menu.

3.   Select **Probability Distributions**.

4.   Select **Binomial**.

5.   The entries in the dialog box shown below correspond to a binomial distribution with $n = 5$, $p = 0.60$ (the probability of success for one trial). The probability values are to be computed for the values of x that have been entered in column C1, and the results will be stored in column C2.

After clicking on **OK**, the probabilities will be displayed in column C2, as shown below. (The column headings of *x* and *P*(*x*) were manually entered.)

x	P(x)
0	0.01024
1	0.07680
2	0.23040
3	0.34560
4	0.25920
5	0.07776

From this display, we see that $P(0) = 0.01024$, $P(1) = 0.07680$, and so on. The preceding example requires the probability that exactly 3 of 5 adults believe in the devil, and the result is $P(3) = 0.346$ (rounded).

5-3 Poisson Distributions

Textbooks in the Triola Statistics Series (except for *Essentials of Statistics*) discuss the Poisson distribution. A Poisson distribution is a discrete probability distribution that applies to occurrences of some event *over a specified interval*. The random variable x is the number of occurrences of the event in an interval, such as time, distance, area, volume, or some similar unit. The probability of the event occurring x times over an interval is given by this formula:

$$P(x) = \frac{\mu^x \cdot e^{-\mu}}{x!} \qquad \text{where } e \approx 2.71828$$

The textbook also notes that the Poisson distribution is sometimes used to approximate the binomial distribution when $n \geq 100$ and $np \leq 10$; in such cases, we use $\mu = np$. If using Minitab, the method of using the Poisson approximation to the binomial distribution isn't used much, because we can easily find binomial probabilities for a wide range of values for n and p, so an approximation method is not necessary.

Minitab Procedure for Finding Probabilities for a Poisson Distribution

1. Determine the value of the mean μ.

2. In column C1, enter the values of the random variable x for which you want probabilities. (You can enter values of x as 0, 1, 2, ...)

3. Click on **Calc** from the main menu.

4. Select **Probability Distributions**.

5. Select **Poisson**.

6. You will now see a dialog box like the one shown below. The probability values are to be computed for the values of x that have been entered in column C1, and the results will be stored in column C2.

Let's consider Atlantic hurricanes occurring so that the mean number of hurricanes is 6.1 per year. If we want the probabilities corresponding to $x = 0, 1, 2, 3, 4, 5$ hurricanes in a year, enter the values of 0, 1, 2, 3, 4, 5 in column C1. The resulting probabilities are shown on the next page.

This is the Minitab result showing the probabilities calculated using the Poisson distribution. Additional values of x could have been entered, and the corresponding probabilities would have been found.

x	P(x)
0	0.002243
1	0.013681
2	0.041729
3	0.084848
4	0.129393
5	0.157860

5-4 Cumulative Probabilities

The main objective of this section is to stress the point that *cumulative probabilities* are often critically important. By *cumulative* probability, we mean the probability that the random variable x has a range of values instead of a single value. Here are typical examples:

- Find the probability of getting *at least* 13 girls in 14 births.
- Find the probability of *more than* 5 wins when roulette is played 200 times.

A *cumulative* probability is often much more important than the probability of any individual event. Section 5-1 of the textbook includes criteria for determining when results are *significantly high* or *significantly low*, and the following criteria involve cumulative probabilities.

Using Probabilities to Determine When Results Are Significant
---

- **Significantly *high* number of successes:** x successes among n trials is a *significantly high* number of successes if the probability of x or more successes is 0.05 or less.

  That is, x is a significantly high number of successes if $P(x \text{ or more}) \le 0.05$.[*]

- **Significantly *low* number of successes:** x successes among n trials is a *significantly low* number of successes if the probability of x or fewer successes is 0.05 or less.

  That is, x is a significantly low number of successes if $P(x \text{ or fewer}) \le 0.05$.[*]

[*]The value 0.05 is not absolutely rigid. Other values, such as 0.01, could be used to distinguish between results that are significant and those that are not significant.

Consider the results consisting of 879 girls in 945 births in clinical trials of the XSORT method of gender selection. Is 879 girls in 945 births a significantly high number of girls? What does it suggest about the effectiveness of the XSORT method of gender selection?

Here we want the cumulative probability of getting 879 or more girls, assuming that boys and girls are equally likely. Using Minitab with the methods in Section 5-2 of this manual/workbook, we find that the probability of 879 or more girls is 0.000 when rounded to three decimal places. This indicates that 879 girls in 945 is a significantly high number of girls, suggesting that the XSORT method of gender selection is effective. Here, cumulative probabilities play a critical role in identifying results that are considered to be *significant*. Later chapters focus on this important concept. If you examine the dialog boxes used for finding binomial probabilities and Poisson probabilities, you can see that in addition to obtaining probabilities for specific numbers of successes, you can also obtain *cumulative* probabilities.

CHAPTER 5 EXPERIMENTS: Probability Distributions

5-1. ***Genetic Disorder*** Three males with an X–linked genetic disorder have one child each. The random variable x is the number of children among the three who inherit the X–linked genetic disorder, and the probability distribution for that number of children is given in the table below.

x	$P(x)$
0	0.4219
1	0.4219
2	0.1406
3	0.0156

Use Minitab with the procedure described in Section 5-1 of this manual/workbook for the following.

Find the mean and standard deviation:

Mean:_____ St. Dev.:_____

5-2. ***Overbooked Flights.*** Air America has a policy of routinely overbooking flights. The random variable x represents the number of passengers who cannot be boarded because there are more passengers than seats (based on data from an IBM research paper by Lawrence, Hong, and Cherrier).

x	$P(x)$
0	0.051
1	0.141
2	0.274
3	0.331
4	0.187

Use Minitab with the procedure described in Section 5-1 of this manual/workbook for the following.

Find the mean and standard deviation:

Mean:_____ St. Dev.:_____

5-3.   ***Genetics.*** Groups of five babies are randomly selected. In each group, the random
        variable x is the number of babies with green eyes (base on data from a study by Dr.
        Sorita Soni at Indiana University). (The symbol 0+ denotes a positive probability value
        that is very small.)

x	$P(x)$
0	0.528
1	0.360
2	0.098
3	0.013
4	0.001
5	0+

Use Minitab with the procedure described in Section 5-1 of this manual/workbook for the
following.

Find the mean and standard deviation:

Mean:_____ St. Dev.:_____

5-4.   ***Binomial Probabilities***   Use Minitab to find the binomial probabilities corresponding to $n =$
        4 and $p = 0.05$. Enter the results below, along with the corresponding results found in Table
        A-1 of the textbook.

x $P(x)$ from Minitab $P(x)$ from Table A-1

0

1

2

3

4

By comparing the above results, what advantage does Minitab have over Table A-1?

_____

_____

5-5.   ***Binomial Probabilities***   Consider the binomial probabilities corresponding to $n = 4$ and $p =$ 1/4 (or 0.25). If you attempt to use Table A-1 for finding the probabilities, you will find that the table does not apply to a probability of $p = 1/4$. Use Minitab to find the probabilities and enter the results below.

$P(0) =$ _____

$P(1) =$ _____

$P(2) =$ _____

$P(3) =$ _____

$P(4) =$ _____

5-6.   ***Binomial Probabilities***   Assume that boys and girls are equally likely and 100 births are randomly selected. Use Minitab with $n = 100$ and $p = 0.5$ to find $P(x)$, where x represents the number of girls among the 100 babies.

$P(35) =$ _____

$P(45) =$ _____

$P(50) =$ _____

5-7.   ***Cumulative Probabilities***   Assume that $P(\text{boy}) = 0.5121$, $P(\text{girl}) = 0.4879$, and that   100

births are randomly selected. Use Minitab to find the probability that the number of   girls

among 100 babies is . . .

a.   Fewer than 60   _____

b.   Fewer than 48   _____

c.   At most 30   _____

d.   At least 55   _____

e.   More than 40   _____

5-8.   ***Identifying 0+***   In Table A-1 from the textbook, the probability corresponding to $n = 7$, $p =$ 0.95, and $x = 2$ is shown as 0+. Use Minitab to find the corresponding probability and enter the result here.   _____

5-9.   ***Identifying 0+***   In Table A-1 from the textbook, the probability corresponding to $n = 8$, $p =$ 0.01, and $x = 6$ is shown as 0+. Use Minitab to find the corresponding probability and enter the result here.   _____

5-10. *Identifying a Probability Distribution* Use Minitab to construct a table of *x* and *P*(*x*) values corresponding to a binomial distribution in which $n = 5$ and $p = 0.35$. Enter the table in the space below.

Table:

Binomial. *Exercises 5–11 through 5-15 involve binomial distributions. Use Minitab for those exercises.*

5-11. *Brand Recognition* The brand name of Mrs. Fields (cookies) has a 90% recognition rate (based on data from Franchise Advantage). If Mrs. Fields herself wants to verify that rate by beginning with a small sample of ten randomly selected consumers, find the probability that exactly nine of the ten consumers recognize her brand name. Also find the probability that the number who recognize her brand name is *not* nine.

_____

5-12. *Too Young to Tat* Based on a Harris poll, among adults who regret getting tattoos, 20% say that they were too young when they got their tattoos. Assume that 5 adults who regret getting tattoos are randomly selected, and find the indicated probability.

a. Find the probability that none of the selected adults say that they were too young to get tattoos. _____

b. Find the probability that exactly one of the selected adults says that they were too young to get tattoos. _____

c. Find the probability that the number of selected adults saying they were too young is 0 or 1. _____

5-13. *Eye Color* In the United States, 40% of the population have brown eyes (based on data from Dr. P Sorita Soni at Indiana University). If 14 people are randomly selected, find the probability that at least 12 of them have brown eyes. Is it unusual to randomly select 14 people and find that at least 12 of them have brown eyes? Why or why not?

_____

5-14. *Credit Rating* There is a 1% delinquency rate for consumers with FICO (Fair Isaac & Company) credit rating scores above 800. If the Jefferson Valley Bank provides large loans to 12 people with FICO scores above 800, what is the probability that at least one of them becomes delinquent? Based on that probability, should the bank plan on dealing with a delinquency?

_____

5-15. *Genetics* Ten peas are generated from parents having the green/yellow pair of genes, so there is a 0.75 probability that an individual pea will have a green pod. Find the probability that among the 10 offspring peas, at least nine have green pods. Is it unusual to get at least nine peas with green pods when ten offspring peas are generated? Why or why not?

_____

Poisson *Exercises 5-16 through 5-18 involve Poisson distributions. Use Minitab for these exercises.*

5–16. *Radioactive Decay* Radioactive atoms are unstable because they have too much energy. When they release their extra energy, they are said to decay. When studying Cesium 137, it is found that during the course of decay over 365 days, 1,000,000 radioactive atoms are reduced to 977,287 radioactive atoms.
   a.   Find the mean number of radioactive atoms lost through decay in a day. _____
   b.   Find the probability that on a given day, 50 radioactive atoms decayed.   _____

5-17. *Chocolate Chip Cookies* In the production of chocolate chip cookies, we can consider each cookie to be the specified "interval unit" required for a Poisson distribution, and we can consider the variable *x* to be the number of chocolate chips in a cookie. The Appendix B data set "Chocolate Chip Cookies" includes the numbers of chocolate chips in 34 different Keebler cookies, and they have a mean of 30.4 chocolate chips. The Poisson distribution requires a value for μ, so use 30.4, which is the mean number of chocolate chips in the 34 Keebler cookies. Assume that the Poisson distribution applies.

   a. Find the probability that a cookie will have 26 chocolate chips. _____
   b. Find the probability that a cookie will have 30 chocolate chips. _____

5-18. *Deaths From Horse Kicks* A classic example of the Poisson distribution involves the number of deaths caused by horse kicks of men in the Prussian Army between 1875 and 1894. Data for 14 corps were combined for the 20-year period, and the 280 corps-years included a total of 196 deaths. After finding the mean number of deaths per corps-year, find the probability that a randomly selected corps-year has the following numbers of deaths.
   a. 0 _____   b. 1 _____   c. 2 _____   d. 3 _____   e. 4 _____
   The actual results consisted of these frequencies: 0 deaths (in 144 corps-years); 1 death (in 91 corps-years); 2 deaths (in 32 corps-years); 3 deaths (in 11 corps-years); 4 deaths (in 2 corps-years). Compare the actual results to those expected from the Poisson probabilities. Does the Poisson distribution serve as a good device for predicting the actual results?

_____

_____

6

Normal Distributions

6-1 Finding Areas and Values with a Normal Distribution

The Triola textbook describes methods for working with standard and nonstandard normal distributions. (A **standard normal distribution** has a mean of 0 and a standard deviation of 1.) Table A-2 in Appendix B of the textbook lists a wide variety of different z scores along with their corresponding areas. Minitab can also be used to find probabilities associated with the normal distribution. Although Table A-2 in the textbook includes only limited values of z scores and their corresponding areas, Minitab can be used with infinitely many different possible choices. In the following procedure, note that like Table A-2 in the textbook, Minitab areas are to the *left* of the related x value. Here is the procedure for finding areas similar to those in the body of Table A-2 from the textbook.

Minitab Procedure for Finding Areas and Values with a Normal Distribution

1. Select **Calc** from the main menu at the top of the screen.

2. Select **Probability Distributions** from the subdirectory.

3. Select **Normal**.

4. You will get a dialog box like the one shown below.

When making choices and entries in the dialog box, consider the following:

- **Probability density** is the height of the normal distribution curve, so we will rarely use this option.

- **Cumulative probability:** Use this option to find an area or probability. Note that you will get the area under the curve to the *left* of the x value(s) entered in column C1. (You must have already entered the x value(s) in column C1, or you could enter a constant value of x by selecting the **Input constant** option.)

- **Inverse cumulative probability:** Use this option to find a value corresponding to a given area. The resulting x value(s) separates an area to the *left* that is specified in column C1. (You must have already entered the cumulative left areas in column C1, or you could enter a single area as a constant by selecting the **Input constant** option.)

The input column is the column containing values (either areas or x values) that you have already entered, and the output column is the column that will list the results (either x values or areas).

5. Click **OK** and the results will be listed in the output column.

Examples: Assume that IQ scores are normally distributed with a mean of 100 and a standard deviation of 15.

- **Finding Area:** To find the area to the left of 115, enter 115 in column C1, then select **Calc, Probability Distributions**, then **Normal**. In the dialog box, select the option of **Cumulative Probability** (because you want an *area*). The result will be 0.843415, which is the area to the *left* of 115.

- **Finding a Value:** To find the 90th percentile, enter 0.9 in column C1, then select **Calc, Probability Distributions**, then **Normal**. In the dialog box, select the option of **Inverse Cumulative Probability** (because you want a *value* of IQ score). The result will be 119.223, which is the IQ score separating an area of 0.9 to its *left*.

6-2 Simulating and Generating Normal Data

We can learn much about the behavior of normal distributions by analyzing samples obtained from them. Sampling from real populations is often time consuming and expensive, but we can use the wonderful power of computers to obtain samples from theoretical normal distributions, and Minitab has such a capability, as described below. Let's consider IQ scores. IQ tests are designed to produce a mean of 100 and a standard deviation of 15, and we expect that such scores are normally distributed. Suppose we want to learn about the variation of sample means for samples of IQ scores. Instead of going out into the world and randomly selecting groups of people and administering IQ tests, we can sample from theoretical populations. We can then learn much about the distribution of sample means. The following procedure allows you to obtain a random sample from a normally distributed population with a given mean and standard deviation.

Generating a Random Sample from a Normally Distributed Population

1. Click on the main menu item of **Calc**.

2. Click on **Random Data**.

3. Click on **Normal**.

4. You will now get a dialog box such as the one shown below. You must enter the population mean and standard deviation. The entries in the dialog box below result in a simulated sample of 500 IQ scores taken from a population with a normal distribution that has a mean of 100 and a standard deviation of 15. The sample values are stored in column C1.

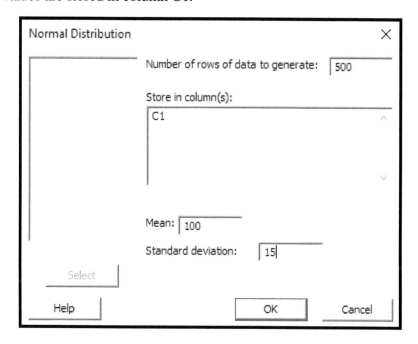

Important: *When using the above procedure, the generated sample will not have a mean equal to the specified population mean, and the standard deviation of the sample will not have a value equal to the specified standard deviation.* When the author generated 500 sample values with the above dialog box, he obtained sample values with a mean of 100.28 and a standard deviation of 13.98. Remember, you are sampling from a population with the specified parameters; you are not generating a sample with statistics exactly equal to the specified values.

6-3 The Central Limit Theorem

The textbook introduces the central limit theorem, which is then used in subsequent chapters when the important topics of estimating parameters and hypothesis testing are discussed. Here is the statement of the central limit theorem in the Triola textbook:

The Central Limit Theorem and the Sampling Distribution of $\bar{x}$

Given:
1. The random variable x has a distribution (which may or may not be normal) with mean μ and standard deviation σ.
2. Simple random samples all of the same size n are selected from the population. (The samples are selected so that all possible samples of size n have the same chance of being selected.)

Conclusions:
1. The distribution of sample means $\bar{x}$ will, as the sample size increases, approach a *normal* distribution.
2. The mean of all sample means is the population mean μ.
3. The standard deviation of all sample means is $\sigma/\sqrt{n}$.

Practical Rules Commonly Used

1. If the original population is *not normally distributed*, here is a common guideline: For $n > 30$, the distribution of the sample means can be approximated reasonably well by a normal distribution. (There are exceptions, such as populations with very nonnormal distributions requiring sample sizes larger than 30, but such exceptions are relatively rare.) The distribution of sample means gets closer to a normal distribution as the sample size n becomes larger.

2. If the original population is *normally distributed*, then for *any* sample size n, the sample means will be normally distributed.

Illustration of the Central Limit Theorem In the study of methods of statistical analysis, it is extremely helpful to have a clear understanding of the statement of the central limit theorem. It is helpful to use Minitab in conducting an experiment that illustrates the central limit theorem. For example, let's use Minitab to generate five columns of data randomly selected with Minitab's **Integer** distribution, which generates integers so that they are all equally likely. After generating 5000 values (each between 0 and 9) in each of columns C1, C2, C3, C4, and C5, we will stack the

25,000 values in column C6. We will also calculate the 5000 sample means of the values in the rows of columns C1, C2, C3, C4, and C5 and enter the results in column C7. (The sample means can be obtained by selecting **Calc,** then selecting **Row Statistics**; select **Mean** and enter C1-C7 for Input variables.) See the histograms shown below. The first histogram shows the distribution of the 25,000 generated integers, but the second histogram shows the distribution of the 5000 sample means (one mean from each row of $n = 5$ values). We can clearly see that the sample means have a distribution that is approximately normal, even though the original population has a uniform distribution.

6-4 Assessing Normality

Textbooks in the Triola statistics series discuss criteria for determining whether sample data appear to come from a population having a normal distribution. These criteria are listed:

1. **Histogram:** Construct a Histogram. Reject normality if the histogram departs dramatically from a bell shape. Minitab can generate a histogram. Section 2-2 of this manual/workbook gives the Minitab procedure for generating a histogram.

2. **Outliers:** Identify outliers. Reject normality if there is more than one outlier present. (Just one outlier could be an error or the result of chance variation, but be careful, because even a single outlier can have a dramatic effect on results.) Using Minitab, we can sort the data and easily identify any values that are far away from the majority of all other values. Minitab-generated boxplots can also be used to identify potential outliers. Section 3-3 of this manual/workbook provides the Minitab procedure for generating a "modified boxplot." Modified boxplots are described in Part 2 of Section 3-3 in the textbook. In a Minitab-generated boxplot, points identified with asterisks are potential outliers.

3. **Normal Quantile Plot:** If the histogram is basically symmetric and there is at most one outlier, construct a *normal quantile plot*. Examine the normal quantile plot and reject normality if the points do not lie close to a straight line, or if the points exhibit some systematic pattern that is not a straight-line pattern. Minitab can generate a *normal probability plot*, which can be interpreted the same way as the normal quantile plot described in the textbook. (Select **Stat**, then **Basic Statistics**, then **Normality Test**.) Also, a normal probability plot can be generated with "percentile" curves that serve as boundaries for departures from normal distributions. (Select **Graph**, then **Probability Plot**, and select the option of **Single**.)

Also, Part 2 of Section 6-6 in the Triola textbook includes a brief reference to the Ryan-Joiner test as one of several formal tests of normality, each having their own advantages and disadvantages. Minitab includes the Ryan-Joiner test, the Anderson-Darling test, and the Kolmogorov-Smirnov test as formal tests that can be used for assessing the normality of a data set. Any one of these three normality tests can be conducted by selecting **Stat**, then **Basic Statistics**, then **Normality Test**.

Normal Probability Plot To obtain a normal probability plot, click on the main menu item of **Stat**, then select **Basic Statistics**, then **Normality Test**. You will get a dialog box like the one shown below. The entries in the window at the left are present because the worksheet "Alcohol and Tobacco in Movies" was opened so that columns with numerical data are listed. Click on the desired column so that its label appears in the "Variable" box. Click **OK**. The resulting normal quantile plot will be as shown on the bottom of this page.

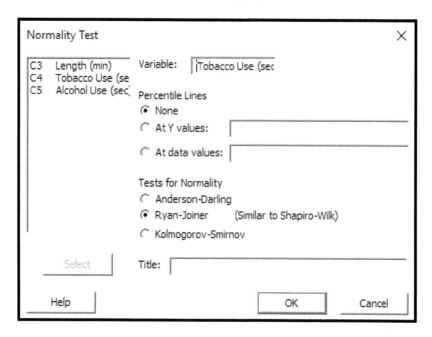

Using the normal probability plot shown below, we see that the plot does *not* yield a pattern of points that reasonably approximates a straight line, so we conclude that the times for tobacco use are not normally distributed.

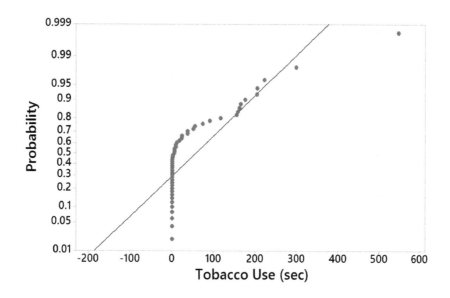

Shown below is the normal probability plot obtained by selecting **Graph**, **Probability Plot**, and **Single**. See that boundary lines are included. Because the points extend beyond those boundary lines, we conclude that the distribution of data is not a normal distribution.

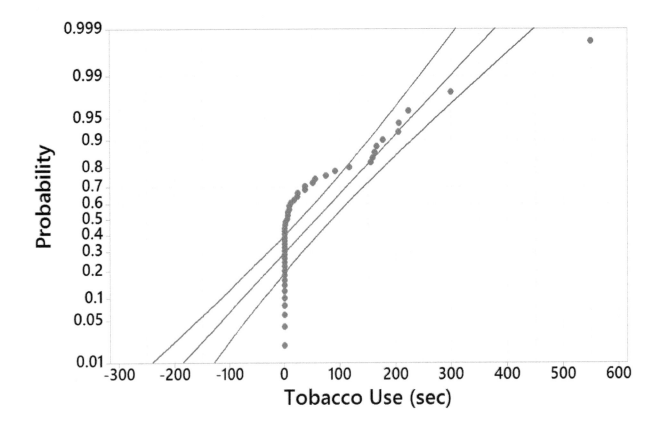

6-5 Normal Approximation to Binomial

Section 6-6 in the Triola textbook discusses the topic of using a normal distribution as an approximation to a binomial distribution. Note the following comment:

> Instead of using a normal distribution as an *approximation* to a binomial
> probability distribution, most practical applications of the binomial distribution
> can now be directly handled with computer software or a calculator.

When working with applications involving a binomial distribution, Minitab can usually be used to find *exact* results, so there is no need to approximate the binomial distribution with a normal distribution. Consequently, the method of using a normal approximation to a binomial distribution is a method that is becoming obsolete. Consider the following example:

In one of Mendel's famous hybridization experiments, he expected that among 580 offspring peas, 145 of them (or 25%) would be yellow, but he actually got 152 yellow peas. Assuming that Mendel's rate of 25% is correct, find the probability of getting 152 or more yellow peas by random chance. That is, given $n = 580$ and $p = 0.25$, find P(at least 152 yellow peas). Is 152 yellow peas *significantly high?*

Based on the above statements, we have $n = 580$ and $p = 0.25$, and we want to find $P(x \geq 152)$, which is the probability of getting 152 or more yellow peas by chance among the 580 peas that are produced. Using Minitab with the binomial distribution procedure described in Section 5-2 of this manual/workbook, we can find that the probability of 151 or fewer yellow peas is 0.735044, so the *exact* probability of 152 or more yellow peas is $1 - 0.735044 = 0.264956$. This is a more accurate result than the result of 0.2665 found by using the normal distribution as an approximation to the binomial distribution. We therefore recommend this strategy:

**Solve binomial distribution problems by getting *exact* results from
Minitab instead of using a normal approximation to a binomial distribution.**
(Use **Calc, Probability Distributions, Binomial** as described in Section 5-2
of this manual/workbook.)

CHAPTER 6 EXPERIMENTS: Normal Distributions

6-1.   *Finding Probabilities for a Normal Distribution*   Use Minitab's **Normal** probability distribution module to find the indicated probabilities. First select **Calc** from the main menu, then select **Probability Distributions**, then **Normal**. Probabilities can be found by using the **Cumulative Probability** option. Remember that like Table A-2 in the textbook, Minitab's probabilities correspond to cumulative areas from the *left*.

   a.   Given a population with a normal distribution, a mean of 0, and a standard deviation of 1, find the probability of a value less than 0.75._____

   b.   Given a population with a normal distribution, a mean of 100, and a standard deviation of 15, find the probability of a value less than 83._____

   c.   Given a population with a normal distribution, a mean of 120, and a standard deviation of 10, find the probability of a value greater than 135._____

   d.   Given a population with a normal distribution, a mean of 98.6, and a standard deviation of 0.62, find the probability of a value between 97.0 and 99.0._____

   e.   Given a population with a normal distribution, a mean of 150, and a standard deviation of 12, find the probability of a value between 147 and 160._____

6-2.   *Finding Values for a Normal Distribution*   Use Minitab's **Normal** module to find the indicated vales. First select **Calc** from the main menu, then select **Probability Distributions**, then **Normal**. Values can be found by using the **Inverse cumulative probability** option. Remember that like Table A-2 in the textbook, Minitab's probabilities correspond to cumulative areas from the left.

   a.   Given a population with a normal distribution, a mean of 0, and a standard deviation of 1, what value has an area of 0.4 to its left?_____

   b.   Given a population with a normal distribution, a mean of 100, and a standard deviation of 15, what value has an area of 0.3 to its right?_____

   c.   Given a population with a normal distribution, a mean of 85, and a standard deviation of 8, what value has an area of 0.95 to its left?_____

   d.   Given a population with a normal distribution, a mean of 45.5, and a standard deviation of 3.5, what value has an area of 0.88 to its right?_____

   e.   Given a population with a normal distribution, a mean of 94, and a standard deviation of 6, what value has an area of 0.01 to its left?_____

6-3. *Central Limit Theorem* In this experiment we will illustrate the central limit theorem. See the example in Section 6-3 of this manual/workbook.

    a.   Use Minitab to create columns C1, C2, C3, C4, and C5 so that each column contains 250 values that are randomly generated integers between 0 and 9.

    b.   Use **Data/Stack** to stack all of the 1250 values in column C6. Obtain a printed copy of the histogram for the sample data in column C6. Also find the mean and standard deviation of the 1250 values and enter the results here.

        Mean:_____   Standard deviation:_____

    c.   Now create a column C7 consisting of the 250 sample means. The first entry of column C7 is the mean of the first entries in columns C1 through C5, the second entry of C7 is the mean of the second entries in columns C1 through C5, and so on. (Click on **Calc**, select **Row Statistics**, select **Mean**, and enter C1-C5 for the input variables. Enter C7 as the column for storing the results.) Obtain a printed copy of the histogram for the sample data in column C7. Also find the mean and standard deviation and enter those values here.

        Mean:_____   Standard deviation:_____

    d.   How do these results illustrate the central limit theorem?

        _____

        _____

6-4. *Central Limit Theorem* In this experiment we will illustrate the central limit theorem. See the example in Section 6-3 of this manual/workbook.

    a.   Use Minitab to create columns C1 through C20 in such a way that each column contains 5000 values that are randomly generated from Minitab's **Uniform** distribution with a minimum of 0 and a maximum of 5.

    b.   Stack all of the sample values in column C21. [See part (b) of the preceding exercise.] Obtain a printed copy of the histogram for the sample data in column C21. Also find the mean and standard deviation and enter those values here.

        Mean:_____   Standard deviation:_____

    c.   Now create a column C22 consisting of the 5000 sample means. The first entry of column C22 is the mean of the first entries in columns C1 through C20, the second entry of C22 is the mean of the second entries in columns C1 through C20, and so on. [See part (c) of the preceding exercise.]
Obtain a printed copy of the histogram for the sample data in column C22. Also find the mean and standard deviation and enter those values below.

        Mean:_____   Standard deviation:_____

d.   How do these results illustrate the central limit theorem?

_____

_____

6-5.   *Identifying Significance* People generally believe that the mean body temperature is 98.6°F. The "Body Temperatures" data set in Appendix B of the textbook includes a sample of 106 body temperatures with these properties: The distribution is approximately normal, the sample mean is 98.20°F, and the standard deviation is 0.62°F. We want to determine whether these sample results differ from 98.6°F by a *significant* amount. One way to make that determination is to study the behavior of samples drawn from a population with a mean of 98.6 (and a standard deviation of 0.62°F and a normal distribution).

a.   Use Minitab to generate 106 values from a normally distributed population with a mean of 98.6 and a standard deviation of 0.62. Use **Stat/Basic Statistics/Display Descriptive Statistics** to find the mean of the generated sample. Record that mean here:_____

b.   Repeat part (a) nine more times and record the 10 sample means here:

_____

c.   By examining the 10 sample means in part b, we can get a sense for how much sample means vary for a normally distributed population with a mean of 98.6 and a standard deviation of 0.62. After examining those 10 sample means, what do you conclude about the likelihood of getting a sample mean of 98.20? Is 98.20 a sample mean that could easily occur by chance, or is it significantly different from the likely sample means that we expect from a population with a mean of 98.6?

_____

_____

d.   Given that researchers did obtain a sample of 106 temperatures with a mean of 98.20°F, what does their result suggest about the common belief that the population mean is 98.6°F?

_____

_____

6-6. **_Identifying Significance_** This experiment involves one of the data sets in Appendix B of the textbook: "Cola Weights and Volumes."

a. Open the worksheet and find the mean and standard deviation of the sample consisting of the volumes of cola in cans of regular Coke. Enter the results here. Sample mean:_____ Standard deviation:_____

b. Generate 10 different samples, where each sample has 36 values randomly selected from a normally distributed population with a mean of 12 oz and a standard deviation of 0.115 oz (based on the claimed volume printed on the cans and the data in Appendix B). For each sample, record the sample mean and enter it here.

_____

c. By examining the 10 sample means in part b, we can get a sense for how much sample means vary for a normally distributed population with a mean of 12 and a standard deviation of 0.115. After examining those 10 sample means, what do you conclude about the likelihood of getting a sample mean like the one found for the sample volumes in Appendix B? Is the mean for the sample a value that could easily occur by chance, or is it significantly different from the likely sample means that we expect from a population with a mean of 12?

_____

d. Consider the sample mean found from the volumes of regular Coke listed in Appendix B from the textbook. Does it suggest that the population mean of 12 oz (as printed on the label) is not correct?

_____

Assessing Normality. _In the following exercises, refer to the indicated data set and use Minitab to determine whether the data have a normal distribution. Give a reason explaining your choice._

6-7. **_Birth Weights_** The birth weights listed in the "Births" dataset in Appendix B of the textbook.

6-8. **_Earthquake Magnitudes_** The magnitudes of the earthquakes, as listed in the "Earthquakes" dataset in Appendix B of the textbook.

6-9. **_Heights of Females_** The measured heights of females, as listed in the "Body Data" dataset in Appendix B of the textbook.

6-10. **_Heights of Males_** The measured heights of males, as listed in the "Body Data" dataset in Appendix B of the textbook.

7

Confidence Intervals and Sample Sizes

7-1 Confidence Intervals for Estimating *p*

Section 7-1 of the Triola textbook presents methods for using a sample proportion to estimate a population proportion, and a confidence interval is a common and important tool used for that purpose. A **confidence interval** (or **interval estimate**) is a range (or an interval) of values used to estimate the true value of a population parameter.

Important note about the Minitab methods: Section 7-1 in the textbook gives a method for constructing a confidence interval estimate of a population proportion *p*. The textbook procedure is based on the use of a normal distribution as an approximation to a binomial distribution. However, *Minitab uses a different method that is much more complex, but Minitab's method should provide better results.* Minitab does also provide an option for using the normal approximation method.

- **Minitab's default method for generating a confidence interval estimate of a population proportion *p* is different from the normal approximation described in Section 7-1 of the textbook.**

- **Minitab's method for generating a confidence interval for *p* includes an option for using the same normal distribution approximation method described in Section 7-2 of the textbook.**

Finding *x*: Minitab requires the sample size *n* and the number of successes *x* to construct a confidence interval estimate of a population proportion *p*. In some cases, the values of *x* and *n* are both known, but in other cases the given information may consist of *n* and a sample percentage. For example, suppose we know that among 1007 people surveyed, 85% said that they know what Twitter is. Based on that information, we know that $n = 1007$ and $\hat{p} = 0.85$. Finding the value of *x* is quite simple: 85% of 1007 = 0.85 × 1007 = 856 (rounded to a whole number). (Because $\hat{p} = x/n$, it follows that $x = \hat{p}n$, so the number of successes can be found by multiplying the sample proportion *p* and the sample size *n*.)

To find the number of successes *x* from the sample proportion and sample size: Calculate $x = \hat{p} \cdot n$ and round the result to the nearest whole number.

After having determined the value of the sample size *n* and the number of successes *x*, we can proceed to use Minitab as follows.

Minitab Procedure for Obtaining Confidence Interval Estimates of *p*

1. Select **Stat** from the main menu.

2. Select **Basic Statistics**.

3. Select **1 Proportion**.

4. You will get a dialog box like the one that follows. In the top box, it is almost always best to select the option of **Summarized data**.

5. In the "Number of events" box, enter the value of *x*, and in the "Number of trials box," enter the value of *n*. The entries shown below correspond to $x = 856$ and $n = 1007$.

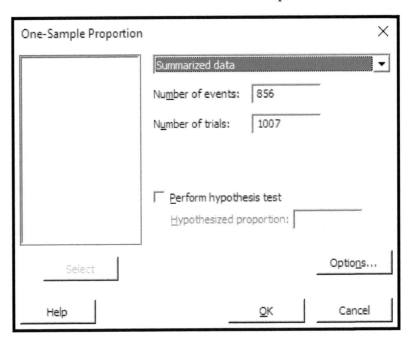

5.   Click on **Options** to change the confidence level from 95% to any other value.

6.   The "Method" box gives you two options: (1) Exact; (2) normal approximation. The normal approximation method uses the same procedure given in the textbook, but the "exact" procedure gives more accurate results.

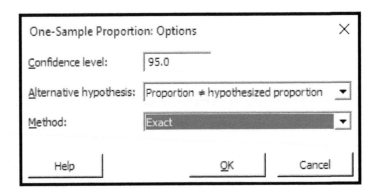

After clicking **OK**, Minitab's *exact* results are as shown below.

Test and CI for One Proportion

Sample	X	N	Sample p	95% CI
1	856	1007	0.850050	(0.826482, 0.871549)

Based on the above Minitab display, we can express the 95% confidence interval estimate of p as $0.826 < p < 0.872$. If you choose the option of using the normal distribution approximation method, Minitab will provide the confidence interval of $0.828 < p < 0.872$. In this case (but not all cases), the result is very close to the result obtained using the exact method.

7-2 Confidence Intervals for Estimating μ

Section 7-2 in the textbook introduces a method for using a sample mean $\bar{x}$ to estimate the value of a population mean μ. Consider the following weights (hectograms or hg) of randomly selected girls at birth, based on data from the National Center for Health Statistics. Here are the summary statistics: $n = 15$, $\bar{x} = 30.9$ hg, $s = 2.9$ hg. We want to use the sample data to construct a 95% confidence interval for the mean birth weight of girls.

33 28 33 37 31 32 31 28 34 28 33 26 30 31 28

Part 1 of Section 7-2 in the textbook focuses on the case in which the population standard deviation σ is not known, as is usually the case. Here is the procedure for using Minitab to construct confidence interval estimates of a population mean μ.

Minitab Procedure for Obtaining Confidence Intervals for μ

1. Select **Stat** from the main menu.

2. Select **Basic Statistics** from the subdirectory.

3. Select **1-Sample t** (or select **1-Sample z** if σ is known, which is rare.)

4. You will now see a dialog box, such as the one shown below.

    Top entry box: For the sample data, you can use either the original list of sample values by selecting **One or more samples, each in a column**, or you can use the summary statistics by selecting **Summarized data**.

    Enter the label of the column containing the list of data or enter the summary statistics (sample size n, sample mean $\bar{x}$, sample standard deviation s). In the following screen display, the column named "Weight" containing the 15 birth weights listed above is used.

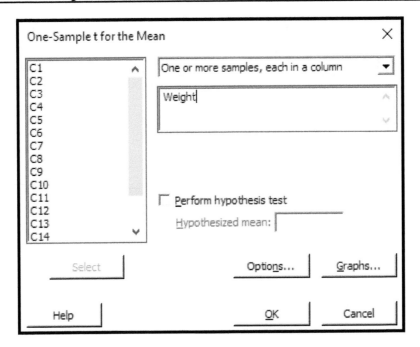

5.   Click on the **Options** box to enter the confidence level. (The Minitab default is a confidence level of 95%.) Also confirm that the "Alternative hypothesis" box includes the expression with the ≠ symbol. Click **OK** when done.

After clicking **OK** on the above screen, you get the following Minitab display.

```
One-Sample T: Weight

Variable    N     Mean   StDev   SE Mean       95% CI
Weight     15   30.867   2.924     0.755   (29.247, 32.486)
```

Based on the above Minitab display, the 95% confidence interval is 29.2 hg $< \mu <$ 32.5 hg (rounded). We are 95% confident that the limits of 29.2 hg and 32.5 hg actually do contain the value of the population mean μ.

7-3 Confidence Intervals for Estimating σ

Let's again use the following weights (hectograms or hg) of randomly selected girls at birth, based on data from the National Center for Health Statistics. Here again are the summary statistics: $n = 15$, $\bar{x} = 30.9$ hg, $s = 2.9$ hg. We want to use the sample data to construct a 95% confidence interval for the standard deviation of the birth weights of girls.

33 28 33 37 31 32 31 28 34 28 33 26 30 31 28

Here is the Minitab procedure for constructing confidence interval estimates of a population standard deviation σ or a population variance σ^2.

Minitab Procedure for Confidence Intervals for Estimating σ

1.   Enter the original sample values in a Minitab column, or obtain the values of the sample size n and the sample standard deviation s (or the sample variance s^2).

2.   Select **Stat** from the main menu.

3.   Select **Basic Statistics** from the subdirectory.

4.   Select **1 Variance**.

5.   You will get a dialog box like the one shown below. In the top box, click on the triangle icon at the right and select one of these three options:
     One or more samples, each in a column   (for a list of sample data)
     Sample standard deviation   (if the value of s is known.)
     Sample variance   (if the value of s^2 is known.)

6.   Either enter the label of the column containing the sample data or enter the required sample statistics, then click **OK**.

5. Click on the **Options** box to enter the confidence level. (The Minitab default is a confidence level of 95%.) Also confirm that the "Alternative hypothesis" box includes the expression with the $\neq$ symbol. Click **OK** when done. See the results shown below.

```
Test and CI for One Variance: Weight

Method

The chi-square method is only for the normal
distribution.
The Bonett method is for any continuous distribution.

Statistics

Variable   N  StDev  Variance
Weight     15  2.92     8.55

95% Confidence Intervals
                         CI for           CI for
Variable  Method          StDev           Variance
Weight    Chi-Square   (2.14, 4.61)    (4.58, 21.27)
          Bonett       (2.10, 4.69)    (4.41, 21.95)
```

The method described in Section 7-3 of the textbook is based on the chi-square distribution, so here we will use the results based on that method; we therefore have this 95% confidence interval estimate of the population standard deviation: 2.1hg $< \sigma <$ 4.6 hg.

7-4 Bootstrap Resampling

Section 7-4 of the textbook describes procedures for the bootstrap resampling method of constructing confidence interval estimates of population parameters. Minitab 17 does not yet have a function for generating bootstrap samples, but Minitab Express does have a bootstrap capability. It is very likely that after Minitab Release 17, the next release will include a bootstrap function.

In Minitab Express, click on the **Statistics** tab, then click on the **Resampling** icon, then proceed to select the bootstrapping options that include **1-Sample Proportion, 1-Sample Mean,** and **2-Sample Means.** Proceed to complete the dialog box to get a confidence interval estimate of the chosen parameter.

Listed below are eruption times (seconds) of the Old Faithful geyser in Yellowstone National Park. If we list these times in column C1 of Minitab Express and use the above procedure, we get the results shown on the next page. Based on this display, the 95% confidence interval estimate of μ is 233.78 sec $< \mu <$ 244.94 sec.

125 203 205 221 225 229 233 233 235 236 236 237 238 238 239 240 240 240 240 241
241 242 242 242 243 243 244 245 245 245 245 246 246 248 248 248 249 249 250 251
252 253 253 255 255 256 257 258 262 264

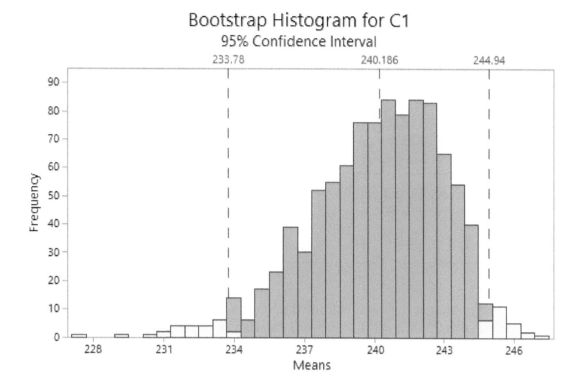

7-5 Determining Sample Sizes

The textbook discuss procedures for determining sample sizes necessary to estimate a population proportion p, or mean μ, or standard deviation σ.

Minitab Procedure for Determining Sample Sizes

   1. Select **Stat** from the main menu.

   2. Select the submenu item of **Power and Sample Size.**

   3. Select **Sample Sizes for Estimates.**

   4. In the top box, use the arrow icon to select the desired parameter to be estimated (mean, standard deviation, variance, proportion).

Note: If "proportions" is selected, enter a known value of $\hat{p}$ for the "Planning Value," and if no value of $\hat{p}$ is known, enter 0.5 for the planning value. Because an estimate of a proportion is found using a binomial distribution instead of an approximating normal distribution, estimated sample sizes from Minitab will be somewhat different from those calculated using the method described in the textbook.

CHAPTER 7 EXPERIMENTS: Confidence Intervals and Sample Sizes

In Experiments 7–1 through 7–4, use Minitab with the sample data and confidence level to construct the confidence interval estimate of the population proportion p.

7-1.   From a KRC Research poll in which respondents were asked if they felt vulnerable to identify theft: $n = 1002$, $x = 531$ who said "yes". Use a 95% confidence level.

_____

7-2.   From a 3M Privacy Filters poll in which respondents were asked to identify their favorite seat when they fly: $n = 806$, $x = 492$ who chose the window seat. Use a 99% confidence level.

_____

7-3.   From a Prince Market Research poll in which respondents were asked if the acted to annoy a bad driver: $n = 2518$, $x = 1083$ who said that they honked. Use a 90% confidence level.

_____

7-4.   From an Angus Reid Public Opinion poll in which respondents were asked if they felt that U. S. nuclear weapons made them feel safer: $n = 1005$, $x = 543$ who said "yes". Use a confidence level of 80%.

_____

In Experiments 7–5 through 7–14, use Minitab with the sample data and confidence level to construct the confidence interval estimate of the population mean μ.

7–5. $n = 50$, $\overline{x} = 75$, $s = 12$; 95% confidence   _____

7–6. $n = 87$, $\overline{x} = 62.3$, $s = 6.6$; 95% confidence   _____

7–7. $n = 32$, $\overline{x} = 8.92$, $s = 1.33$; 99% confidence   _____

7–8. $n = 106$, $\overline{x} = 98.2$, $s = 0.62$; 99% confidence   _____

7–9. $n = 81$, $\overline{x} = 12.8$, $s = 2.7$; 95% confidence   _____

7–10. $n = 212$, $\overline{x} = 1008.1$, $s = 47.3$; 95% confidence   _____

7–11. $n = 212$, $\bar{x} = 625$, $s = 38$; 95% confidence _____

7–12. $n = 53$, $\bar{x} = 57$, $s = 7$; 95% confidence _____

7–13. $n = 71$, $\bar{x} = 82.4$, $s = 11.2$; 95% confidence _____

7–14. $n = 150$, $\bar{x} = 9.9$, $s = 2.7$; 95% confidence _____

7–15. ***Mendelian Genetics*** When Mendel conducted his famous genetics experiments with peas, one sample of offspring consisted of 428 green peas and 152 yellow peas.

    a.   Use Minitab to find the following confidence interval estimates of the percentage of yellow peas.
        99.5% confidence interval: _____
        99% confidence interval: _____
        98% confidence interval: _____
        95% confidence interval: _____
        90% confidence interval: _____

    b.   After examining the pattern of the above confidence intervals, complete the following statement. "As the degree of confidence decreases, the confidence interval limits …

_____."

    c.   In your own words, explain why the preceding completed statement makes sense. That is, why should the confidence intervals behave as you have described?

_____

_____

7-16. ***Gender Selection*** The Genetics and IVF Institute conducted a clinical trial of the XSORT method designed to increase the probability of conceiving a girl. As of this writing, 945 babies were born to parents using the XSORT method, and 879 of them were girls.

    a.   What is the best point estimate of the population proportion of girls born to parents using the XSORT method? _____

    b.   Use the sample data to construct a 95% confidence interval estimate of the percentage of girls born to parents using the XSORT method.

_____

(continued)

c.   Based on the results, does the XSORT method appear to be effective? Why or why not?

_____

_____

_____

7-17.   *Gender Selection* The Genetics and IVF Institute conducted a clinical trial of the YSORT method designed to increase the probability of conceiving a boy. As of this writing, 291 babies were born to parents using the YSORT method, and 239 of them were boys.

a.   What is the best point estimate of the population proportion of boys born to parents using the YSORT method? _____

b.   Use the sample data to construct a 99% confidence interval estimate of the percentage of boys born to parents using the YSORT method.

_____

c.   Based on the results, does the YSORT method appear to be effective? Why or why not?

_____

_____

7-18.   *Touch Therapy* When she was nine years of age, Emily Rosa did a science fair experiment in which she tested professional touch therapists to see if they could sense her energy field. She flipped a coin to select either her right hand or her left hand, then she asked the therapists to identify the selected hand by placing their hand just under Emily's hand without seeing it and without touching it. Among 280 trials, the touch therapists were correct 123 times (based on data in "A Close Look at Therapeutic Touch," *Journal of the American Medical Association*, Vol. 279, No. 13).

a.   Given that Emily used a coin toss to select either her right hand or her left hand, what proportion of correct responses would be expected if the touch therapists made random guesses? _____

b.   Using Emily's sample results, construct a 99% confidence interval estimate of the proportion of correct responses made by touch therapists.

_____

c.   What do the results suggest about the ability of touch therapists to select the correct hand by sensing an energy field?

_____

In Exercises 7-19 through 7-22, use the data sets from Appendix B in the textbook.

7-19. *Nicotine in Cigarettes* Refer to the "Cigarette Contents" dataset in Appendix B of the textbook and assume that the samples are simple random samples obtained from normally distributed populations.

a. Construct a 95% confidence interval estimate of the mean amount of nicotine in cigarettes that are king size, non-filtered, non-menthol, and non-light.

_____

b. Construct a 95% confidence interval estimate of the mean amount of nicotine in cigarettes that are 100 mm, filtered, non-menthol, and non-light.

_____

c. Compare the results. Do filters on cigarettes appear to be effective?

_____

_____

7-20. *Pulse Rates* A physician wants to develop criteria for determining whether a patient's pulse rate is atypical, and she wants to determine whether there are significant differences between males and females. Use the sample pulse rates in the "Body Data" dataset from Appendix B in the textbook.

a. Construct a 95% confidence interval estimate of the mean pulse rate for males.

_____

b. Construct a 95% confidence interval estimate of the mean pulse rate for females.

_____

c. Compare the preceding results. Can we conclude that the population means for males and females are different? Why or why not?

_____

_____

_____

7-21.   ***Weights of Coins*** Refer to the weights of pre-1964 quarters and the weights of post-1964 quarters listed in the "Coin Weights" dataset from Appendix B of the textbook.

   a.   Construct a 95% confidence interval estimate of the mean weight of pre-1964 quarters.

   _____

   b.   Construct a 95% confidence interval estimate of the mean weight of post-1964 quarters.

   _____

   c.   Compare the preceding results. Can we conclude that the population means for pre-1964 quarters and post-1964 quarters are different? Why or why not?

   _____

   _____

7-22.   ***Second Hand Smoke*** Refer to the measured cotinine levels of smokers, nonsmokers exposed to cigarette smoke, and nonsmokers not exposed to cigarette smoke. The cotinine measurements are listed in "Passive and Active Smoke" dataset from Appendix B of the textbook.

   a.   Construct a 95% confidence interval estimate of the mean cotinine level of smokers.

   _____

   b.   Construct a 95% confidence interval estimate of the mean cotinine level of nonsmokers exposed to cigarette smoke.

   _____

   c.   Construct a 95% confidence interval estimate of the mean cotinine level of nonsmokers not exposed to cigarette smoke.

   _____

   d.   Compare the preceding results. What do you conclude?

   _____

   _____

   _____

7-23. ***Simulated Data*** Minitab is designed to generate random numbers from a variety of different sampling distributions. In this experiment we will generate 500 IQ scores, then we will construct a confidence interval based on the sample results. IQ scores have a normal distribution with a mean of 100 and a standard deviation of 15. First generate the 500 sample values as follows.

    1.   Click on **Calc,** then select **Random Data**, then **Normal**.

    2.   In the dialog box, enter a sample size of 500, a mean of 100, and a a standard deviation of 15. Specify column C1 as the location for storing the results. Click **OK**.

    3.   Use **Stat/Basic Statistics/Display Descriptive Statistics** to find these statistics:

$n =$ _____ $\overline{x} =$ _____ $s =$ _____

Using the generated values, construct a 95% confidence interval estimate of the population mean of all IQ scores. Enter the 95% confidence interval here.

_____

Because of the way that the sample data were generated, we *know* that the population mean is 100. Do the confidence interval limits contain the true mean IQ score of 100?___

If this experiment were to be repeated many times, how often would we expect the confidence interval limits to contain the true population mean value of 100? Explain how you arrived at your answer.

_____

_____

7-24. ***Simulated Data*** Follow the same steps listed in Experiment 7-23 to randomly generate 500 IQ scores from a population having a normal distribution, a mean of 100, and a standard deviation of 15. Record the sample statistics here.

$n =$ _____ $\overline{x} =$ _____ $s =$ _____

Confidence intervals are typically constructed with confidence levels around 90%, 95%, or 99%. Instead of constructing such a typical confidence interval, use the generated values to construct a 50% confidence interval. Enter the result below.

_____

Does the above confidence interval have limits that actually do contain the true population mean, which we know is 100? _____

(continued)

Repeat the above procedure 9 more times and list the resulting 50% confidence intervals here.

_____   _____

_____   _____

_____   _____

_____   _____

_____

Among the total of the 10 confidence intervals constructed, how many of them actually do contain the true population mean of 100? Is this result consistent with the fact that the level of confidence used is 50%? Explain.

_____

_____

7-25.   ***Combining Data Sets***   Refer to the "M&M Weights: dataset in Appendix B of the textbook and use the entire sample of 100 plain M&M candies to construct a 95% confidence interval for the mean weight of all M&Ms. The Minitab worksheet is M&M. It is not necessary to manually enter the 100 weights, because they are already stored in separate Minitab columns in the worksheet M&M. (*Hint:* Select **Data,** then use **Stack** to combine the different M&M data sets into one big data set.) Now construct a 95% confidence interval estimate of the population mean of all IQ scores. Enter the 95% confidence interval here.

_____

7-26.   ***Combining Data Sets***   Refer to the "Word Counts" dataset in Appendix B of the textbook. Combine all of the word counts from males in one column, and combine all of the word counts from females in another column. (*Hint:* Select **Data,** then select **Stack.**)

a.   Find the 95% confidence interval estimate of the mean word count for men.

_____

b.   Find the 95% confidence interval estimate of the mean word count for women.

_____

c.   Based on the results, does it appear that either gender talks more than the other? Why or why not?

_____

_____

In Exercises 7-27 through 7-30, use the data sets from Appendix B in the textbook to construct confidence interval estimates of the population standard deviations.

7-27. *Nicotine in Cigarettes* Refer to "Cigarette Contents" dataset in Appendix B of the textbook and assume that the samples are simple random samples obtained from normally distributed populations.

    a.   Construct a 95% confidence interval estimate of the standard deviation of amounts of nicotine in cigarettes that are king size, non-filtered, non-menthol, and non-light. _____

    b.   Construct a 95% confidence interval estimate of the standard deviation of amounts of nicotine in cigarettes that are 100 mm, filtered, non-menthol, and non-light. _____

    c.   Compare the results. Do the amounts of variation appear to be different?

    _____

    _____

7-28. *Pulse Rates* A physician wants to develop criteria for determining whether a patient's pulse rate is atypical, and she wants to determine whether there are significant differences between males and females. Use the "Body Data" dataset in Appendix B in the textbook.

    a.   Construct a 95% confidence interval estimate of the standard deviation of pulse rates for males.

    _____

    b.   Construct a 95% confidence interval estimate of the standard deviation of pulse rates for females.

    _____

    c.   Compare the preceding results. Do the amounts of variation appear to be different?

    _____

    _____

    _____

    _____

7-29. ***Weights of Coins*** Refer to the weights of pre-1964 quarters and the weights of post-1964 quarters listed in the "Coin Weights" dataset from Appendix B of the textbook.

    a. Construct a 95% confidence interval estimate of the standard deviation of the weights of pre-1964 quarters.

    b. Construct a 95% confidence interval estimate of the standard deviation of the weights of post-1964 quarters.

    c. Compare the preceding results. Do the amounts of variation appear to be different?

7-30. ***Second Hand Smoke*** Refer to the measured cotinine levels of smokers, nonsmokers exposed to cigarette smoke, and nonsmokers not exposed to cigarette smoke. The cotinine measurements are listed in the "Passive and Active Smoke" dataset from Appendix B of the textbook.

    a. Construct a 95% confidence interval estimate of the standard deviation of cotinine levels of smokers.

    b. Construct a 95% confidence interval estimate of the standard deviation of cotinine levels of nonsmokers exposed to cigarette smoke.

    c. Construct a 95% confidence interval estimate of the standard deviation of cotinine levels of nonsmokers not exposed to cigarette smoke.

    d. Compare the preceding results. What do you conclude?

8

Hypothesis Testing

8–1 Minitab's Assistant Feature

Minitab introduced its new *Assistant* feature in Release 16 and it now also available in the latest release. If you click on the main menu item of **Assistant,** you get a submenu with options including these:

> **Graphical Analysis**
> **Hypothesis Tests**
> **Regression**
> **Control Charts**

If you select the submenu item of **Hypothesis Tests,** you get the following display.

You can see that this display is helpful in guiding you to choose the correct method. For the purposes of Chapter 8 in the textbook, we would like to compare one sample with a target, so the top arrows guide us to the leftmost column of choices. (You could also click on **Help me choose** to obtain further guidance.) If you want to test a claim about a population proportion, select the item labeled **1 Sample % Defective**. You will get a dialog box that asks for more information in a simpler format, and after entering the information about the sample, you will get *three* screens of results that provide much information that is helpful in interpreting your results. Here is an example of the first screen:

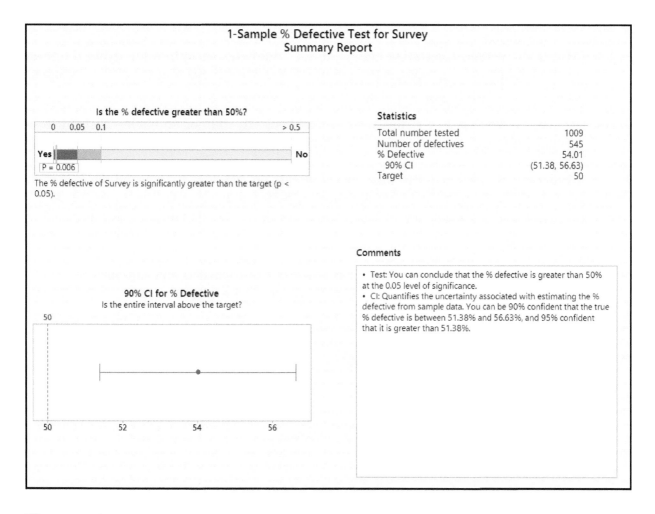

The screen includes a comment that "You can conclude that the % defective is greater than 50% at the 0.05 level of significance." Another comment describes a confidence interval and provides 90% confidence interval limits. (The confidence level of 90% is appropriate for a right-tailed hypothesis test with a 0.05 significance level.) In general, Minitab's *Assistant* provides helpful guidance in selecting the correct method and it provides results that are very helpful in analyzing and interpreting the results.

The following sections of this manual/workbook describe the use of Minitab's basic functions, but consider using the *Assistant* feature in place of those basic methods.

8–2 Testing Hypotheses About p

Important note about the Minitab methods: Section 8-2 in the textbook gives a method for testing a claim about a population proportion p. The textbook procedure is based on the use of a normal distribution as an approximation to a binomial distribution. However, *Minitab uses a different method that is much more complex, but Minitab's method should provide better results.* Minitab does provide an option for using the normal approximation method.

- **Minitab's default method for testing claims about a population proportion p is different from the normal approximation described in Section 8-2 of the textbook.**

- **Minitab's method for testing claims about p includes an option for using the same normal distribution approximation method described in Section 8-2 of the textbook.**

The Minitab procedure for testing claims about a population proportion follows the same basic steps described in Section 7–1 of this manual/workbook. In addition to having a claim to be tested, Minitab also requires a significance level, the sample size n, and the number of successes x.

      Finding x: In Section 7-1 of this manual/workbook, we briefly discussed one particular difficulty that arises when the available information provides the sample size n and the sample proportion $\hat{p}$ instead of the number of successes x. We provided this procedure for determining the number of successes x.

> **To find the number of successes x from the sample proportion and sample size:**
> **Calculate $x = \hat{p}n$ and round the result to the nearest whole number.**

Given a claim about a proportion and knowing n and x, we can use Minitab as follows.

Minitab Procedure for Testing Claims about p

1. Select **Stat** from the main menu.

2. Select **Basic Statistics** from the subdirectory.

3. Select **1 Proportion**.

4. You will get a dialog box.

   - In the top box, click on the triangle icon at the right of the box, then select the option for **Summarized data**.
   - In the box for the "Number of events" (or successes), enter the number of successes x.
   - In the box for "Number of trials," enter the value of the sample size n.
   - Click on the box to select "Perform hypothesis test."
   - In the box labeled "Hypothesized proportion," enter the value of the population proportion used in the null hypothesis.

- Click on the **Options** bar and make the entries in the dialog box:
  i. Enter the confidence level. (Enter 95 for a 0.05 significance level.)
  ii. In the "Alternative hypothesis" box, select the format of the alternative hypothesis.
  iii. In the "Method" box, select either "Exact" (for more accurate results) or select "Normal approximation" (to get results using the method described in Section 8-2 of the textbook.
- Click **OK**.

For example, let's use the sample data of $n = 1009$ and $x = 545$ to test the claim that $p > 0.5$. The dialog boxes and Minitab results are as follows.

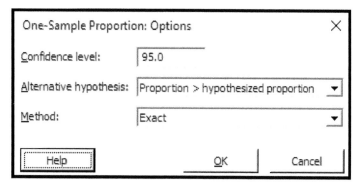

We can see from the displayed results that the *P*-value is 0.006, which causes us to reject the null hypothesis. There is sufficient evidence to support the claim that $p > 0.5$.

Normal Approximation Method: If we had told Minitab to conduct the test using the normal distribution approximation method, the *P*-value would have been 0.005 instead of 0.006.

8–3 Testing Hypotheses About μ

Section 8-3 in the textbook describes details for methods of testing claims about a population mean μ. Part 1 of Section 8-3 focuses on the realistic case in which the population standard deviation σ is not known, and Part 2 briefly considers the somewhat artificial case in which σ is somehow known.

Minitab allows us to test claims about a population mean μ by using either the list of original sample values or the summary statistics of n, $\overline{x}$, and s.

Minitab Procedure for Testing Claims About μ

1. Select **Stat** from the main menu.

2. Select **Basic Statistics** from the subdirectory.

3. Select either **1-Sample t** (or **1-Sample z** if σ is known, which is rare).

4. You will now see a dialog box, such as the one shown below. In the top box, click on the triangle icon at the right of the box, then select "**One or more samples, each in a column**" (for using a list of sample data) or select the option for **Summarized data** (for using the summary statistics of n, $\overline{x}$, s).

5. Click on the box to select "**Perform hypothesis test.**"

6. In the box labeled "**Hypothesized mean,**" enter the value of the population mean used in the null hypothesis.

8. Click on the **Options** button to get the options dialog box, and make the entries according to the following.

   i. Enter the confidence level. (Enter 95 for a 0.05 significance level.)
   ii. In the "Alternative hypothesis" box, select the format of the alternative hypothesis.

9. Click **OK,** then click **OK** on the main dialog box.

As an illustration, consider this example:

> **Cell Phone Radiation** Listed below are measured radiation emissions (in W/kg) from a sample of cell phones (based on data are from the Environmental Working Group). Use a 0.05 significance level to test the claim that cell phones have a mean radiation level less than 1.00 W/kg.
>
> 0.38 0.55 1.54 1.55 0.50 0.60 0.92 0.96 1.00 0.86 1.46

Because $n \leq 30$, we must verify that the sample data appear to be from a normally distributed population, and a quantile plot suggests that this requirement is met. Because σ is not known, use Minitab's **1-Sample t** (instead of 1-Sample z). First enter the sample data in column C1, then proceed to conduct the t test by using the following dialog boxes that correspond to the above example. See that the first dialog box includes the entry of column C1 containing the list of sample values and the box for conducting a hypothesis test is checked, and the value of 1.00 is entered. (The claim of a mean "less than 1.00 W/kg" indicates that the null hypothesis is $H_0: \mu = 1.00$ W/kg, so 1.00 is the hypothesized mean.) The second dialog box shows the confidence level of 95, which corresponds to a 0.05 significance level, and the second dialog box also shows the choice of "less than" for the form of the alternative hypothesis.

We get these Minitab results:

```
One-Sample T: Radiation

Test of μ = 1 vs < 1

Variable    N    Mean   StDev   SE Mean   95% Upper Bound      T       P
Radiation   11   0.938  0.423    0.127               1.169   -0.48   0.319
```

From the above Minitab display, we see that the test statistic is $t = -0.48$. The P-value is 0.319. Because the P-value is greater than the significance level of 0.05, we fail to reject the null hypothesis and conclude that there is not sufficient evidence to support the claim that the population mean is less than 1.00 W/kg.

8-4 Testing Hypotheses About σ or σ^2

When testing claims about σ or σ^2, the textbook stresses that there are the following two important requirements:

1. The samples are simple random samples. (Remember the importance of good sampling methods.)

2. The sample values come from a population with a *normal distribution*.

The textbook makes the very important point that *for tests of claims about standard deviations or variances, the requirement of a normal distribution is very strict*. If the population does not have a normal distribution, then inferences about standard deviations or variances can be very misleading. *Suggestion:* Given sample data, assess normality by using the methods from Section 6-4 of this manual/workbook. If the population distribution does appear to have a normal distribution and you want to test a claim about the population standard deviation or variance, use the Minitab procedure given below.

Minitab Procedure for Testing Claims about σ or σ^2

1. Select **Stat** from the main menu.

2. Select **Basic Statistics** from the subdirectory.

3. Select **1 Variance**.

4. You will get a dialog pop-up screen. In the top box, click on the triangle icon at the right and select one of these three options:
One or more samples, each in a column	(for a list of sample data)
Sample standard deviation	(if the value of s is known.)
Sample variance	(if the value of s^2 is known.)

5.   Either enter the label of the column containing the sample data or enter the required sample statistics, then click **OK**.

6.   Click on the box labeled "**Perform hypothesis test.**"

7.   In the "Hypothesized standard deviation" box, enter the claimed value of the population standard deviation.

8.   Click on the **Options** button to get the Options dialog box, and make the entries according to the following.

   • Enter a confidence level. (Enter 95 for a hypothesis test conducted with a 0.05 significance level.)

   • Click on the "Alternative hypothesis" and select the format used in the alternative hypothesis.

   • Click **OK** when done.

9.   Click **OK** on the main dialog box.

As an illustration, consider this example:

> **Supermodel Heights** Listed below are the heights (inches) for the simple random sample of supermodels. Consider the claim that supermodels have heights that have less variation than heights of women in the general population. We will use a 0.01 significance level to test the claim that supermodels have heights with a standard deviation that is less than 2.6 in. for the population of women.
>
> 70   71   69.25   68.5   69   70   71   70   70   69.5

From the above example, we see that we want to test the claim that $\sigma < 2.6$ in., and we want to use a 0.01 significance level. The normality of the population is verified with a normal quantile plot. We can proceed with the hypothesis test, and the Minitab dialog boxes are shown below, followed by the test results.

In the first dialog box, see that we chose the option of "**One or more samples, each in a column**" because the data were entered as a list in column C1 of Minitab. Also, the "Perform hypothesis test" box is checked, and the value of 2.6 is entered in the "Value" box. (The value of 2.6 is from the claim that $\sigma < 2.6$ in.)

In the second dialog box, the confidence level of 99 was entered (for the significance level of 0.01), and the format of "less than" was chosen for the alternative hypothesis.

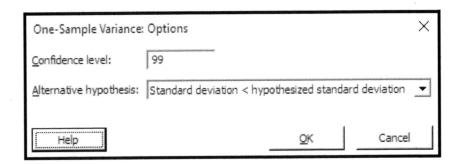

The Minitab results on the next page include the test statistic of $\chi^2 = 0.85$ and *P*-value of 0.000. (The actual *P*-value is 0.000290, but it becomes 0.000 when rounded to three decimal places. Because the *P*-value is low, we reject the null hypothesis and conclude that there is sufficient evidence to support the claim that the population standard deviation σ is less than 2.6 in. (The bottom line includes results from application of Bonnett's method, which is not discussed in the textbook.)

```
Test and CI for One Variance: Height

Method

Null hypothesis        σ = 2.6
Alternative hypothesis σ < 2.6

The chi-square method is only for the normal distribution.
The Bonett method is for any continuous distribution.

Statistics

Variable   N  StDev  Variance
Height     10 0.800    0.640

99% One-Sided Confidence Intervals

                     Upper Bound    Upper Bound
Variable   Method    for StDev    for Variance
Height     Chi-Square    1.660         2.757
           Bonett        1.721         2.961

Tests
                          Test
Variable   Method    Statistic  DF  P-Value
Height     Chi-Square    0.85    9    0.000
           Bonett        −       −    0.001
```

8-5   Testing Hypotheses with Simulations

Sections 8-1, 8-2, 8-3, and 8-4 of this manual/workbook have all focused on using Minitab for hypothesis tests using the *P*-value approach. Another very different approach is to use *simulations*. Let's illustrate the simulation technique with an example.

Consider testing the claim that the population of body temperatures of healthy adults has a mean less than 98.6°F. That is, consider the claim that $\mu < 98.6$°F. We will use sample data consisting of these 12 body temperatures (°F):

98.0 97.5 98.6 98.8 98.0 98.5 98.6 99.4 98.4 98.7 98.6 97.6

For these 12 values, $n = 12$, $\bar{x} = 98.39167$, and $s = 0.53506$. The key question is this:

> If the population mean body temperature is really 98.6, then *how likely* is it that we would get a sample mean of 98.39167, given that the population has a normal distribution and the sample size is 12?

If the probability of getting a sample mean such as 98.39167 is very small, then that suggests that the sample values are not the result of chance random fluctuation. If the probability is high, then we can accept random chance as an explanation for the discrepancy between the sample mean of 98.39167 and the assumed mean of 98.6. What we need is some way of determining the likelihood of getting a sample mean such as 98.39167. That is the precise role of *P*-values in the *P*-value approach to hypothesis testing. However, there is another approach. Minitab and many other software packages are capable of generating random results from a variety of different populations. Here is how Minitab can be used: Determine the likelihood of getting a sample mean of 98.39167 by randomly generating different samples from a population that is normally distributed with the claimed mean of 98.6. For the standard deviation, we will use the best available information: the value of *s* = 0.53506 obtained from the sample.

Minitab Procedure for Testing Hypotheses with Simulations

1. Identify the values of the sample size *n*, the sample standard deviation *s*, and the claimed value of the population mean.

2. Click on **Calc**, then select **Random Data**.

3. Click on **Normal.**

4. Generate a sample randomly selected from a normally distributed population with the claimed mean. When making the required entries in the dialog box, use the *claimed* mean, the sample size *n*, and the sample standard deviation *s*.

5. Continue to generate similar samples until it becomes clear that the given sample mean is or is not likely. (Here is one criterion: The given sample mean is *unlikely* if its value or more extreme values occur 5% of the time or less.) If it is unlikely, reject the claimed mean. If it is likely, fail to reject the claimed mean.

For example, here are 20 results obtained from the random generation of samples of size 12 from a normally distributed population with a mean of 98.6 and a standard deviation of 0.53506:

Sample Means

98.754	**98.374**	**98.332**	98.638	98.513
98.551	98.566	98.760	**98.332**	98.603
98.407	98.640	98.655	98.408	98.802
98.505	98.699	98.609	98.206	98.582

Examining the 20 sample means, we see that three of them (displayed in bold) are 98.39167 or lower. Because 3 of the 20 results (or 15%) are at least as extreme as the sample mean of 98.39167, we see that a sample mean such as 98.39167 is *common* for these circumstances. This suggests that a sample mean of 98.39167 is not *significantly* different from the assumed mean of 98.6. We would feel more confident in this conclusion if we had more sample results, so we could continue to randomly generate simulated samples until we feel quite confident in our thinking that a sample mean such as 98.39167 is not an unusual result. It can easily occur as the result of chance random variation. We therefore fail to reject the null hypothesis that the mean equals 98.6. There is not sufficient evidence to support the claim that the mean is less than 98.6.

CHAPTER 8 EXPERIMENTS: Hypothesis Testing

Experiments 8–1 through 8–4 involve claims about proportions. Use Minitab with the normal approximation procedure for the following.

8–1. **Reporting Income** In a Pew Research Center poll of 745 randomly selected adults, 589 said that it is morally wrong to not report all income on tax returns. Use a 0.01 significance level to test the claim that 75% of adults say that it is morally wrong to not report all income on tax returns.

Test statistic: _____   *P*–value: _____

Conclusion in your own words: _____

_____

8–2. **Voting for the Winner** In a presidential election, 308 out of 611 voters surveyed said that they voted for the candidate who won (based on data from ICR Survey Research Group). Use a 0.01 significance level to test the claim that among all voters, the percentage believing that they voted for the winning candidate is equal to 43%, which is the actual percentage of votes for the winning candidate.

Test statistic: _____   *P*–value: _____

Conclusion in your own words: _____

_____

8–3. **Tennis Instant Replay** The Hawk-Eye electronic system is used in tennis for displaying an instant replay that shows whether a ball is in bounds or out of bounds, so players can challenge calls made by referees. In a recent U.S. Open, singles players made 611 challenges and 172 of them were successful with the call overturned. Use a 0.01 significance level to test the claim that fewer than 1/3 of the challenges are successful.

Test statistic: _____   *P*–value: _____

Conclusion in your own words: _____

_____

8–4.   ***Screening for Marijuana Usage*** The company Drug Test Success provides a "1-Panel-THC" test for marijuana usage. Among 300 tested subjects, results from 27 subjects were wrong (either a false positive or a false negative). Use a 0.05 significance level to test the claim that less than 10% of the test results are wrong.

Test statistic: _____   *P*–value: _____

Conclusion in your own words: _____

_____

8-5.   ***Exact Procedure and Normal Approximation***   Repeat Experiment 8-4 by using Minitab's exact procedure. (In the **Options** dialog box, select **Exact** as the method to be used.)

Test statistic: _____   *P*–value: _____

Conclusion in your own words: _____

_____

Compare the exact results to those found by using the normal approximation.

_____

_____

Experiments 8–6 through 8–9 use Minitab with the original list of sample data for testing the given claim about a population mean.

8–6.   ***Earthquake magnitudes*** Use the earthquake magnitudes in the "Earthquakes" data set in Appendix B and test the claim that the population of earthquakes has a mean magnitude greater than 1.00. Use a 0.05 significance level.

Test statistic: _____   *P*–value: _____

Conclusion in your own words: _____

_____

8–7. **Blood Pressure** Use the systolic blood pressure measurements for females listed in the "Body Data" dataset in Appendix B and test the claim that the female population has a mean systolic blood pressure level less than 120.0 mm Hg. Use a 0.05 significance level.

Test statistic: _____   *P*–value: _____

Conclusion in your own words: _____

_____

8–8. **College Weights** Use the September weights of males in the "Freshman 15" dataset from Appendix B and test the claim that male college students have a mean weight that is less than the 83 kg mean weight of males in the general population. Use a 0.01 significance level.

Test statistic: _____   *P*–value: _____

Conclusion in your own words: _____

_____

8-9. **Tornadoes** Use the "Tornadoes" dataset in Appendix B and test the claim that tornadoes have a mean width that is less than 140 yd. Use a 0.01 significance level.

Test statistic: _____   *P*–value: _____

Conclusion in your own words: _____

_____

In Experiments 8–10 through 8–13, test the claim about a population mean.

8–10. **Cigarette Tar** A simple random sample of 25 filtered 100 mm cigarettes is obtained, and the tar content of each cigarette is measured. The sample has a mean of 13.2 mg and a standard deviation of 3.7 mg (based the "Cigarette Contents" dataset in Appendix B). Use a 0.05 significance level to test the claim that the mean tar content of filtered 100 mm cigarettes is less than 21.1 mg, which is the mean for unfiltered king size cigarettes.

Test statistic: _____   *P*–value: _____

Conclusion in your own words: _____

_____

8–11. ***Is the Diet Practical?*** When 40 people used the Weight Watchers diet for one year, their mean weight *loss* was 3.0 lb and the standard deviation was 4.9 lb (based on data from "Comparison of the Atkins, Ornish, Weight Watchers, and Zone Diets for Weight Loss and Heart Disease Reduction," by Dansinger, et al., *Journal of the American Medical Association,* Vol. 293, No. 1). Use a 0.01 significance level to test the claim that the mean weight loss is greater than 0 lb.

Test statistic: _____   *P*–value: _____

Conclusion in your own words: _____

_____

Based on these results, does the diet appear to be effective? Does the diet appear to have practical significance? Explain.

_____

_____

8–12. ***Weights of Pennies*** The U. S. Mint has a specification that pennies have a mean weight of 2.5 g. The "Coin weights" dataset in Appendix B lists the weights (in grams) of 37 pennies manufactured after 1983. Those pennies have a mean weight of 2.49910 g and a standard deviation of 0.01648 g. Use a 0.05 significance level to test the claim that this sample is from a population with a mean weight equal to 2.5 g.

Test statistic: _____   *P*–value: _____

Conclusion in your own words: _____

_____

8–13. ***Analysis of Pennies*** In an analysis investigating the usefulness of pennies, the cents portions of 100 randomly selected credit card charges are recorded. The sample has a mean of 47.6 cents and a standard deviation of 33.5 cents. If the amounts from 0 cents to 99 cents are all equally likely, the mean is expected to be 49.5 cents. Use a 0.01 significance level to test the claim that the sample is from a population with a mean equal to 49.5 cents.

Test statistic: _____   *P*–value: _____

Conclusion in your own words: _____

In Experiments 8–14 through 8–17, use Minitab to test the claim about a standard deviation or variance.

8–14. **Ages of Race Car Drivers** Listed below are the ages (years) of randomly selected race car drivers (based on data reported in *USA Today*). Most people in the general population have ages that vary between 0 and 90 years, so use of the range rule of thumb suggests that ages in the general population have a standard deviation of 22.5 years. Use a 0.01 significance level to test the claim that the standard deviation of ages of all race car drivers is less than 22.5 years.

32 32 33 33 41 29 38 32 33 23 27 45 52 29 25

Test statistic: _____   *P*–value: _____

Conclusion in your own words: _____

_____

8–15. **Highway Speeds** Listed below are speeds (mi/h) measured from southbound traffic on I-280 near Cupertino, California (based on data from SigAlert). This simple random sample was obtained at 3:30 PM on a weekday. Use a 0.05 significance level to test the claim of the highway engineer that the standard deviation of speeds is equal to 5.0 mi/h.

62 61 61 57 61 54 59 58 59 69 60 67

Test statistic: _____   *P*–value: _____

Conclusion in your own words: _____

_____

8-16. **Aircraft Altimeters** The Skytek Avionics company uses a new production method to manufacture aircraft altimeters. A simple random sample of new altimeters resulted in errors listed below. Use a 0.05 level of significance to test the claim that the new production method has errors with a standard deviation greater than 32.2 ft, which was the standard deviation for the old production method. If it appears that the standard deviation is greater, does the new production method appear to be better or worse than the old method? Should the company take any action?

–42 78 –22 –72 –45 15 17 51 –5 –53 –9 –109

Test statistic: _____   *P*–value: _____

Conclusion in your own words: _____

_____

8–17. *IQ of Professional Pilots* The Wechsler IQ test is designed so that the mean is 100 and the standard deviation is 15 for the population of normal adults. Listed below are IQ scores of randomly selected professional pilots. It is claimed that because professional pilots are a more homogeneous group than the general population, they have IQ scores with a standard deviation less than 15. Test that claim using a 0.05 significance level.

121 116 115 121 116 107 127 98 116 101 130 114

Test statistic: _____ P–value: _____

Conclusion in your own words: _____

_____

Simulations. *The following exercises involve the simulation approach to hypothesis testing.*

8–18. *Hypothesis Testing with Simulations* Suppose that we want to use a 0.05 significance level to test the claim that $p > 0.5$ and we have sample data summarized by $n = 100$ and $x = 70$. Use the following Minitab procedure for using a simulation method for testing the claim that $p > 0.5$.

      We assume in the null hypothesis that $p = 0.5$. Working under the assumption that $p = 0.5$, we will generate different samples of size $n = 100$ until we have a sense for the likelihood of getting 70 or more successes. Begin by generating a sample of size 100 as follows: Select **Calc/Random Data/Integer**. In the dialog box, enter 100 for the number of rows, enter C1–C10 for the columns, then enter a minimum of 0 and a maximum of 1. After clicking **OK**, the result will be 10 columns, where each column represents a sample of 100 subjects with a probability of 0.5 of getting a 1 in each cell. Letting 1 represent a success, use **Stat/Basic Statistics/Display Descriptive Statistics** and find the number of samples having a sample proportion of 0.70 or greater.
Enter that result here: _____

What percentage of the simulated samples have a sample proportion of 0.70 or greater? Enter that result here: _____

What does the preceding result suggest about the likelihood of this event:
"When the population proportion p is really equal to 0.5, a sample of size 100 is randomly selected and the sample proportion is 0.70 or greater."

_____

Can we conclude that the probability of a sample proportion of 0.70 or greater is less than or equal to the significance level of 0.05? _____

What is the final conclusion? _____

_____

8–19. ***Hypothesis Testing with Simulations*** Experiment 8–18 used a simulation approach to test a claim. Use a simulation approach for conducting the hypothesis test described in Experiment 8–2. Describe the procedure, results, and conclusions.

_____

_____

_____

_____

8–20. ***Hypothesis Testing with Simulations*** Refer to Experiment 8–10 in this manual/work-book. We want to test the claim that $\mu < 21.1$, and the given sample data can be summarized with these statistics: $n = 25$, $\overline{x} = 13.2$, and $s = 3.7$. Instead of conducting a formal hypothesis test, we will now consider another way of determining whether the sample mean of 13.2 is significantly less than the claimed value of 21.1. We will use a significance level of 0.05 with this criterion:

> *The sample mean of 13.2 is significantly less than 21.1 if there is a 5% chance (or less) that the following event occurs: A sample mean of 13.2 or less is obtained when selecting a random sample of n = 25 values from a normally distributed population with mean μ = 21.1 and standard deviation σ =3.7.*

Use **Calc/Random Data/Normal** to randomly generate a sample of 25 values from a normally distributed population with the assumed mean of 21.1 and a standard deviation of 3.7. Find the mean of the generated sample and record it in the space below. Then generate another sample, and another sample, and continue until you have enough sample means to determine how often a result such as $\overline{x}$ = 13.2 (or less) will occur.

_____

_____

Enter the number of generated samples:_____

How many of the generated samples have a sample mean less than 21.1? _____

What is the proportion of trials in which the sample mean was 21.1 or less? _____

Based on these results, what do you conclude about the claim that $\mu < 21.1$? Explain.

_____

9

Inferences from Two Samples

9–1 Minitab's Assistant Feature

Minitab introduced its new *Assistant* feature in Release 16, and it is currently available. If you click on the main menu item of **Assistant,** you get a submenu that includes the option of **Hypothesis Tests.** If you select Hypothesis Tests, you are given options of comparing one sample with a target (as in Chapter 8), or comparing two samples with each other (as in this Chapter), or comparing more than two samples. Shown below are the choices available under the comparison of two samples with each other, and those choices include the topics covered in this chapter. An advantage of using the Assistant feature is that you are provided with some guidance in choosing the correct method. Also, after entering information about the sample, you will get different screens of results that provide much information that is helpful in interpreting your results. The following sections of this manual/workbook describe the use of Minitab's basic functions, but consider using the *Assistant* feature in place of those basic methods.

9-2 Two Proportions

The textbook makes the point that the section discussing inferences involving two proportions is one of the most important sections in the book because the main objective is to provide methods for dealing with two sample proportions — a situation that is very common in real applications.

To use Minitab, we must first identify the number of successes x_1 and the sample size n_1 for the first sample, and identify x_2 and n_2 for the second sample. Sample data often consist of sample proportions or percentages instead of the actual numbers of successes, so we must know how to determine the number of successes. From $\hat{p}_1 = x_1/n_1$, we know that $x_1 = n_1 \cdot \hat{p}_1$ so that x_1 can be found by multiplying the sample size for the first sample by the sample proportion expressed in decimal form. For example, if 35.2% of 1200 interviewed subjects answer "yes" to a question, we have $n = 1200$ and $x = 1200 \cdot 0.352 = 422.4$, which we round to 422.

After identifying n_1, x_1, n_2, and x_2, proceed with Minitab as follows.

Minitab Procedure for Inferences (Hypothesis Tests and Confidence Intervals) for Two Proportions

To conduct hypothesis tests or construct confidence interval estimates of the difference between two population proportions, use the following procedure.

1. For each sample, find the sample size n and the number of successes x.

2. Select **Stat**, then **Basic Statistics**, then **2 Proportions**.

3. In the top box of the dialog box, click on the triangle icon at the right and select the option of "**Summarized data**" and enter the number of successes (or "events") for each of the two samples, and enter the sample size (or "trials") for each of the two samples. (The numbers of "Events" are the values of x_1 and x_2. The numbers of "Trials" are the values of n_1 and n_2.)

4. Click on the **Options** bar.

    i. Enter the confidence level (enter 95 for a 0.05 significance level).

    ii. If conducting a hypothesis test, enter the claimed value of the difference (usually 0), and select the format for the alternative hypothesis. (See the Minitab screen on the next page where "greater than" is selected for the format of the alternative hypothesis.)

    iii. In the "Test method" box, choose one of the following:

        Estimate the proportions separately (for a *confidence interval*, where you do *not* want to use a pooled estimate of p)

        Use the pooled estimate of the proportion (for a *hypothesis test*, where you do want to use a pooled estimate of p)

As an illustration, consider the following example:

Large Denominations Less Likely to be Spent? The table below lists sample results from a study conducted to determine whether people are less likely to spend money when it is in the form of larger denominations. Use a 0.05 significance level to test the claim that "money in a large denomination is less likely to be spent relative to an equivalent amount in many smaller denominations." That is, test the claim that the proportion of people who spend a $1 bill is less than the proportion who spend 4 quarters.

	Group 1 Subjects Given $1 Bill	*Group 2* Subjects Given 4 Quarters
Spent the money	$x_1 = 12$	$x_2 = 27$
Subjects in Group	$n_1 = 46$	$n_2 = 43$

We can now proceed to use the above Minitab procedure. After selecting **Stat**, **Basic Statistics**, then **2 Proportions**, we make the required entries in the dialog boxes as shown below.

The claim of a lower spending rate for the population given the $1 bill is the claim that $p_1 < p_2$, so we select the option of "less than" for the alternative hypothesis, as shown below. Also, because we are conducting a hypothesis test, the two sample estimates of the two population proportions are *pooled,* so we check the box as shown below.

After clicking on **OK** in both dialog boxes, the Minitab results will be displayed. Shown below are the results from the preceding example and dialog box entries. The results include the test statistic of $z = -3.49$ and the P–value of 0.000. Because the P–value of 0.000 is less than the significance level of 0.05, we reject the null hypothesis and support the claim that those given $1 spend at a rate less than those given 4 quarters.

```
Test and CI for Two Proportions

Sample    X    N    Sample p
1         12   46   0.260870
2         27   43   0.627907

Difference = p (1) - p (2)
Estimate for difference:   -0.367037
95% upper bound for difference:   -0.205664
Test for difference = 0 (vs < 0):   Z = -3.49   P-Value = 0.000

Fisher's exact test: P-Value = 0.000
```

Confidence Intervals: The above Minitab display includes a one–sided confidence interval, but it is based on *pooling* of the two sample proportions. (See Step 5 in the preceding Minitab procedure. Note that we pool the sample proportions only if we are testing a hypothesis; if we are constructing a confidence interval, we should *not* pool the sample proportions.) If we want a confidence interval estimate of the difference between the two population proportions, we should use "not equal" for the alternative hypothesis and we should *not* use pooling. Without pooling, Minitab provides this 90% confidence interval estimate of the difference between the two population proportions: (−0.528410, −0.205664). This can also be expressed as follows:
$-0.528 < p_1 - p_2 < -0.206$ (rounded).

9-3 Two Means: Independent Samples

The textbook notes that two samples are **independent** if the sample values selected from one population are not related to or somehow paired or matched with the sample values selected from the other population. If there is some relationship so that each value in one sample is paired with a corresponding value in the other sample, the samples are **dependent.** Dependent samples are often referred to as **matched pairs,** or **paired samples.**

When testing a claim about the means of two independent samples, or when constructing a confidence interval estimate of the difference between the means of two independent samples, Part 1 in section 9-2 of the textbook describes procedures based on the requirement that the two population standard deviations σ_1 and σ_2 are *not known*, and there is no assumption that $\sigma_1 = \sigma_2$. We focus on the first of the following three cases, and the other two cases are discussed briefly:

1. σ_1 and σ_2 are not known and are not assumed to be equal.
2. It is assumed that $\sigma_1 = \sigma_2$.
3. σ_1 and σ_2 are known.

The first of these three cases is the main focus of Section 9-2 in the textbook, and Minitab handles that first case but, instead of using "the smaller of $n_1 - 1$ and $n_2 - 1$" for the number of degrees of freedom, Minitab calculates the number of degrees of freedom using Formula 9-1 in Section 9-2 of the textbook.

Minitab also provides the option of assuming that $\sigma_1 = \sigma_2$, but there is no option for assuming that σ_1 and σ_2 are *known*. That is, Minitab allows us to deal with cases 1 and 2 listed above, but not case 3. We describe the Minitab procedure, then consider an example.

Minitab Procedure for Inferences (Hypothesis Tests and Confidence Intervals) About Two Means: Independent Samples

Use the following procedure for both hypothesis tests and confidence intervals.

1. Identify the values of the summary statistics, or enter the original sample values in columns C1 and C2 (or open a Minitab worksheet with columns containing the two lists of sample values).

2. Click on the main menu item of **Stat**, select **Basic Statistics**, then **2-Sample t.**

3. Proceed to make the entries in the dialog box.

   - In the top box, select either of these two options:
     Each sample is in its own column (if the lists of sample data are in separate columns)

     Summarized data (if n, $\overline{x}$, s are known for each sample)

   - Complete the initial dialog box by making the entries as required.

4.   Click on the **Options** bar.

      i.   Enter the confidence level (enter 95 for a 0.05 significance level).

      ii.   If conducting a hypothesis test, enter the claimed value of the difference (usually 0), and select the format for the alternative hypothesis.

      iii.   Click **OK** when finished.

5.   Click **OK** on the main dialog box.

As an illustration, consider the following example.

> **Are Men and Women Equal Talkers?** A headline in *USA Today* proclaimed that "Men, women are equal talkers." That headline referred to a study of the numbers of words that samples of men and women spoke in a day. Given below are the results from the study, which are included in the "Word Counts" data set in Appendix B (based on "Are Women Really More Talkative Than Men?" by Mehl, et al, *Science*, Vol. 317, No. 5834). Use a 0.05 significance level to test the claim that men and women speak the same mean number of words in a day. Does there appear to be a difference?

Number of Words Spoken in a Day

Men	Women
$n_1 = 186$	$n_2 = 210$
$\bar{x}_1 = 15{,}668.5$	$\bar{x}_2 = 16{,}215.0$
$s_1 = 8632.5$	$s_2 = 7301.2$

Using Minitab with the preceding procedure, we enter the summary statistics as shown below.

Click on the **Options** button, then make the selections shown in the following dialog box.

The Minitab results are as shown below. The test statistic is $t = -0.68$ and the P-value is 0.500, so we fail to reject the null hypothesis. There is not sufficient evidence to reject the claim that men and women speak the same mean number of words in a day.

```
Two-Sample T-Test and CI

Sample    N    Mean   StDev  SE Mean
1        186  15669   8633     633
2        210  16215   7301     504


Difference = μ (1) - μ (2)
Estimate for difference:   -547
95% CI for difference:   (-2137, 1044)
T-Test of difference = 0 (vs ≠): T-Value = -0.68  P-Value = 0.500  DF = 364
```

Confidence Interval If we wanted to construct a confidence interval for the difference between the mean number of words spoken by men and the mean number of words spoken by women in day, the results above show that the 95% confidence interval is $-2137 < \mu_1 - \mu_2 < 1044$. Because that confidence interval includes 0, there does not appear to be a significant difference between the two means.

9-4 Matched Pairs

The textbook describes methods for testing hypotheses and constructing confidence interval estimates of the differences between samples consisting of *matched pairs*. Here is the Minitab procedure:

Minitab Procedure for Inferences (Hypothesis Tests and Confidence Intervals) About Two Means: Matched Pairs

To conduct hypothesis tests or construct confidence intervals using data consisting of matched pairs, use the following procedure.

1.   Enter the values of the first sample in a column (such as column C1). Enter the values of the second sample in another column (such as C2) (or open a Minitab worksheet that includes columns of matched pairs of sample data).

2.   Select **Stat**, **Basic Statistics**, **Paired t**.

3.   In the top box, select the option of **Each sample is in a column,** which is almost always the better choice.

4.   Click on the **Options** bar and in the Options dialog box, make the following entries:

   i.   Enter the confidence level. (Enter 95 for a 95% confidence interval or a hypothesis test with a 0.05 level of significance.)

   ii.   Enter 0 for the hypothesized difference.

   iii.   Select the correct format for the alternative hypothesis.

   iv.   Click **OK.**

5.   Click **OK** on the main dialog box.

See the following example.

> **Hypothesis Test of Claimed Freshman Weight Gain** Listed below are samples of measured weights of college students in September and April of their freshman year. Use the sample data with a 0.05 significance level to test the claim that for the population of students, the mean change in weight from September to April is equal to 0 kg.

Weight (kg) Measurements of Students in Their Freshman Year

April weight	66	52	68	69	71
September weight	67	53	64	71	70

First enter the April weights in one column, then enter the September weights in another column. Shown below are the dialog boxes and the Minitab results.

Paired T-Test and CI: April, Sept

```
Paired T for April - Sept

              N    Mean   StDev   SE Mean
April         5   65.20    7.60      3.40
Sept          5   65.00    7.25      3.24
Difference    5    0.20    2.39      1.07


95% CI for mean difference: (-2.76, 3.16)
T-Test of mean difference = 0 (vs ≠ 0): T-Value = 0.19  P-Value = 0.861
```

The *P*-value of 0.861 is greater than the significance level of 0.05, so we fail to reject the null hypothesis that the mean of the differences between the April weights and the September weights is equal to 0 kg. Based on the five given pairs of April/September weights, there does not appear to be a significant difference.

Confidence Interval The above Minitab results show that the 95% confidence interval estimate of the mean of the differences is -2.8 kg $< \mu_d < 3.2$ kg (rounded). Because the confidence interval includes 0 kg, there does not appear to be a significant difference.

9-5 Two Variances

The textbook describes the use of the *F* distribution in testing a claim that two populations have the same variance (or standard deviation). Minitab can conduct such an *F* test.

Minitab Procedure for Inferences (Hypothesis Tests and Confidence Intervals) For Two Standard Deviations or Two Variances

1. Either obtain the summary statistics for each sample, or enter the individual sample values in two columns (or open a Minitab worksheet containing the columns of sample data).

2. Select **Stat**, then **Basic Statistics**, then **2 Variances**.

3. A dialog box will appear. In the top box, select one of these options:

   Each sample is in its own column (for data listed in two columns)
   Sample standard deviations (both sample standard deviations are known)
   Sample variances (both sample variances are known)

   Proceed to enter the required items.

4. Click on the **Options** bar and make the following entries.

   i. Choose either option in the top box.

   ii. Enter the confidence level. Enter 95 for a hypothesis test using a 0.05 significance level.

   iii. For the hypothesized ratio, enter 1.

   iv. In the "Alternative hypothesis" box, select the correct format for the alternative hypothesis.

   v. Click **OK.**

5. Click **OK** on the main dialog box.

Consider the following example, which is followed by the key Minitab results obtained by using the above procedure.

> **Comparing Variation in Weights of Quarters** Sample statistics are listed below for weights of quarters made before and after 1964. Use a 0.05 significance level to test the claim that the weights of pre-1964 quarters and the weights of post-1964 quarters are from populations with the same standard deviation.
>
> | Pre-1964 Quarters | Post-1964 Quarters |
> |---|---|
> | $n = 40$ | $n = 40$ |
> | $s = 0.08700$ g | $s = 0.06194$ g |

Minitab Results

Method	DF1	DF2	Test Statistic	P-Value
F	39	39	1.97	0.037

The Minitab results include the P-value of 0.037, which is less than the significance level of 0.05. We therefore reject the null hypothesis that the two populations of quarters have weights with the same standard deviation.

CHAPTER 9 EXPERIMENTS: Inferences from Two Samples

9-1. ***Drug Use in College*** In a 1993 survey of 560 college students, 171 said that they used illegal drugs during the previous year. In a recent survey of 720 college students, 263 said that they used illegal drugs during the previous year (based on data from the National Center for Addiction and Substance Abuse at Columbia University). Use a 0.05 significance level to test the claim that the proportion of college students using illegal drugs in 1993 was less than it is now.

Test statistic: _____ *P*–value: _____

Conclusion in your own words: _____

_____

9-2. ***Drug Use in College*** Using the sample data from Experiment 9-1, construct the confidence interval corresponding to the hypothesis test conducted with a 0.05 significance level. What conclusion does the confidence interval suggest?

_____

_____

9-3. ***Are Seat Belts Effective?*** A simple random sample of front-seat occupants involved in car crashes is obtained. Among 2823 occupants not wearing seatbelts, 31 were killed. Among 7765 occupants wearing seatbelts, 16 were killed (based on data from "Who Wants Airbags?" by Meyer and Finney, *Chance*, Vol. 18, No. 2). Construct a 90% confidence interval estimate of the difference between the fatality rates for those not wearing seat belts and those wearing seat belts. What does the result suggest about the effectiveness of seat belts?

_____

_____

9-4. ***Are Seat Belts Effective?*** Use the sample data in Experiment 9-3 with a 0.05 significance level to test the claim that the fatality rate is higher for those not wearing seat belts.

Test statistic: _____ *P*–value: _____

Conclusion in your own words: _____

_____

_____

9-5.   ***Morality and Marriage*** A Pew Research Center poll asked randomly selected subjects if they agreed with the statement that "It is morally wrong for married people to have an affair." Among the 386 women surveyed, 347 agreed with the statement. Among the 359 men surveyed, 305 agreed with the statement. Use a 0.05 significance level to test the claim that the percentage of women who agree is different from the percentage of men who agree. Does there appear to be a difference in the way women and men feel about this issue?

Test statistic: _____   *P*–value: _____

Conclusion in your own words: _____

_____

9-6.   ***Morality and Marriage*** Using the sample data from Experiment 9-5, construct the confidence interval corresponding to the hypothesis test conducted with a 0.05 significance level. What conclusion does the confidence interval suggest?

_____

_____

9-7.   ***Cardiac Arrest at Day and Night*** A study investigated survival rates for in-hospital patients who suffered cardiac arrest. Among 58,593 patients who had cardiac arrest during the day, 11,604 survived and were discharged. Among 28,155 patients who suffered cardiac arrest at night, 4139 survived and were discharged (based on data from "Survival from In-Hospital Cardiac Arrest During Nights and Weekends," by Peberdy et al., *Journal of the American Medical Association,* Vol. 299, No. 7). Use a 0.01 significance level to test the claim that the survival rates are the same for day and night.

Test statistic: _____   *P*–value: _____

Conclusion in your own words: _____

_____

9-8.   ***Cardiac Arrest at Day and Night*** Using the sample data from Experiment 9-7, construct the confidence interval corresponding to the hypothesis test conducted with a 0.01 significance level. What conclusion does the confidence interval suggest?

_____

_____

In Experiments 9–9 through 9–20, assume that the two samples are independent simple random samples selected from normally distributed populations. Do not assume that the population standard deviations are equal.

9-9.   ***Hypothesis Test of Effectiveness of Humidity in Treating Croup*** Treatment In a randomized controlled trial conducted with children suffering from viral croup, 46 children were treated with low humidity while 46 other children were treated with high humidity. Researchers used the Westley Croup Score to assess the results after one hour. The low humidity group had a mean score of 0.98 with a standard deviation of 1.22 while the high humidity group had a mean score of 1.09 with a standard deviation of 1.11 (based on data from "Controlled Delivery of High vs Low Humidity vs Mist Therapy for Croup Emergency Departments," by Scolnik et al, *Journal of the American Medical Association,* Vol. 295, No. 11). Use a 0.05 significance level to test the claim that the two groups are from populations with the same mean. What does the result suggest about the common treatment of humidity?

Test statistic: _____   *P*–value: _____

Conclusion in your own words: _____

_____

9-10. ***Confidence Interval for Effectiveness of Humidity in Treating Croup*** Use the sample data given in Experiment 9-9 and construct a 95% confidence interval estimate of the difference between the mean Westley Croup Score of children treated with low humidity and the mean score of children treated with high humidity. What does the confidence interval suggest about humidity as a treatment for croup?

_____

_____

9-11. ***Confidence Interval for Cigarette Tar*** The mean tar content of a simple random sample of 25 unfiltered king-size cigarettes is 21.1 mg, with a standard deviation of 3.2 mg. The mean tar content of a simple random sample of 25 filtered 100 mm cigarettes is 13.2 mg with a standard deviation of 3.7 mg (based on data from the "Cigarette Contents" dataset in Appendix B). Construct a 90% confidence interval estimate of the difference between the mean tar content of unfiltered king size cigarettes and the mean tar content of filtered 10mm cigarettes. Does the result suggest that 100 mm filtered cigarettes have less tar than unfiltered king size cigarettes?

_____

_____

9-12. ***Hypothesis Test for Cigarette Tar*** Refer to the sample data in Experiment 9-11 and use a 0.05 significance level to test the claim that unfiltered king size cigarettes have a mean tar content greater than that of filtered 100 mm cigarettes. What does the result suggest about the effectiveness of cigarette filters?

Test statistic: _____   *P*–value: _____

Conclusion in your own words: _____

_____

9-13. ***BMI for Miss America*** The trend of thinner Miss America winners has generated charges that the contest encourages unhealthy diet habits among young women. Listed below are body mass indexes (BMI) for Miss America winners from two different time periods. Consider the listed values to be simple random samples selected from larger populations.

BMI (from recent winners):	19.5 20.3 19.6 20.2 17.8 17.9 19.1
	18.8 17.6 16.8
BMI (from the 1920's and 1930's):	20.4 21.9 22.1 22.3 20.3 18.8 18.9
	19.4 18.4 19.1

a. Use a 0.05 significance level to test the claim that recent winners have a lower mean BMI than winners from the 1920's and 1930's.

Test statistic: _____   *P*–value: _____

Conclusion in your own words: _____

_____

b. Construct a 90% confidence interval for the difference between the mean BMI of recent winners and the mean BMI of winners from the 1920's and 1930's.

_____

_____

9-14. ***Radiation in Baby Teeth*** Listed below are amounts of Strontium-90 (in millibecquerels or mBq per gram of calcium) in a simple random sample of baby teeth obtained from Pennsylvania residents and New York residents born after 1979 (based on data from "An Unexpected Rise in Strontium-90 in U.S. Deciduous Teeth in the 1990s," by Mangano, et. al., *Science of the Total Environment*).

Pennsylvania: 155 142 149 130 151 163 151 142 156 133 138 161

New York: 133 140 142 131 134 129 128 140 140 140 137 143

a. Use a 0.05 significance level to test the claim that the mean amount of Strontium-90 from Pennsylvania residents is greater than the mean amount from New York residents.

Test statistic: _____   *P*–value: _____

Conclusion in your own words: _____

_____

b. Construct a 90% confidence interval of the difference between the mean amount of Strontium-90 from Pennsylvania residents and the mean amount from New York residents.

_____

_____

9-15. ***Longevity*** Listed below are the numbers of years that popes and British monarchs (since 1690) lived after their election or coronation (based on data from *Computer-Interactive Data Analysis*, by Lunn and McNeil, John Wiley & Sons). Treat the values as simple random samples from a larger population.

Popes: 2   9   21   3   6   10   18   11   6   25   23   6   2   15   32   25
                    11   8   17   19   5   15   0   26

Kings and Queens: 17   6   13   12   13   33   59   10   7   63   9   25   36   15

a. Use a 0.01 significance level to test the claim that the mean longevity for popes is less the mean for British monarchs after coronation.

Test statistic: _____   *P*–value: _____

Conclusion in your own words: _____

_____

(continued)

b.   Construct a 98% confidence interval of the difference between the mean longevity of popes and the mean longevity for kings and queens. What does the result suggest about those two means?

_____

_____

9-16. ***Gender and Blood Cell Counts***   White blood cell counts are helpful for assessing liver disease, radiation, bone marrow failure, and infectious diseases. Listed below are white blood cell counts found in simple random samples of males and females (based on data from the Third National Health and Nutrition Examination Survey).

Female: 8.90 6.50 9.45 7.65 6.40 5.15 16.60 5.75 11.60 5.90 9.30 8.55
             10.80 4.85 4.90 8.75 6.90 9.75 4.05 9.05 5.05 6.40 4.05 7.60
             4.95 3.00 9.10
Male: 5.25 5.95 10.05 5.45 5.30 5.55 6.85 6.65 6.30 6.40 7.85 7.70 5.30
             6.50 4.55 7.10 8.00 4.70 4.40 4.90 10.75 11.00 9.60

a.   Use a 0.01 significance level to test the claim that females and males have different mean white blood cell counts.

Test statistic: _____   *P*–value: _____

Conclusion in your own words: _____

_____

b.   Construct a 98% confidence interval of the difference between the mean white blood cell count of females and males. Based on the result, does there appear to be a difference?

_____

_____

9-17. ***Baseline Characteristics***   Reports of results from clinical trials often include statistics about "baseline characteristics," so that we can see that different groups have the same basic characteristics. Refer to the dataset of "Body Data" in Appendix B and construct a 95% confidence interval estimate of the difference between the mean age of men and the mean age of women. Based on the result, does it appear that the sample of men and the sample of women are from populations with the same mean?

Test statistic: _____   *P*–value: _____

Conclusion in your own words: _____

_____

(continued)

    b.   Construct a 95% confidence interval estimate of the difference between the mean age of men and the mean age of women. What does the confidence interval suggest?

_____

_____

9-18   ***Appendix B Data Set: Word Counts*** Refer to the "Word Counts" dataset in Appendix B. Use the word counts for male and female psychology students recruited in Mexico (see the columns labeled M3 and F3).

    a.   Use a 0.05 significance level to test the claim that male and female psychology students speak the same mean number of words in a day.

        Test statistic: _____   *P*–value: _____

        Conclusion in your own words: _____

        _____

    b.   Construct a 95% confidence interval estimate of the difference between the mean number of words spoken in a day by male and female psychology students in Mexico. Do the confidence interval limits include 0, and what does that suggest about the two means?

        _____

        _____

9-19.   ***Appendix B Data Set: Systolic Blood Pressure*** Refer to the "Body Data" dataset in Appendix B. Use a 0.05 significance level to test the claim that females and males have the same mean systolic blood pressure.

        Test statistic: _____   *P*–value: _____

        Conclusion in your own words: _____

        _____

9-20.   ***Appendix B Data Set: Weights of Coke*** Refer to the "Cola Weights and Volumes" in Appendix B and test the claim that because they contain the same amount of cola, the mean weight of cola in cans of regular Coke is the same as the mean weight of cola in cans of Diet Coke. If there is a difference in the mean weights, identify the most likely explanation for that difference.

Test statistic: _____   *P*−value: _____

Conclusion in your own words: _____

_____

9-21.   ***Does BMI Change During Freshman Year?*** Listed below are body mass indices (BMI) of students. The BMI of each student was measured in September and April of the freshman year (based on data from "Changes in Body Weight and Fat Mass of Men and Women in the First Year of College: A Study of the 'Freshman 15'," by Hoffman, Policastro, Quick, and Lee, *Journal of American College Health*, Vol. 55, No. 1). Use a 0.05 significance level to test the claim that the mean change in BMI for all students is equal to 0. Does BMI appear to change during freshman year?

| April BMI | 20.15 | 19.24 | 20.77 | 23.85 | 21.32 |
| September BMI | 20.68 | 19.48 | 19.59 | 24.57 | 20.96 |

Test statistic: _____   *P*−value: _____

Conclusion in your own words: _____

_____

9-22.   ***Confidence Interval for BMI Changes*** Use the same paired data from Experiment 9-21 to construct a 95% confidence interval estimate of the change in BMI during freshman year. Does the confidence interval include 0, and what does that suggest about BMI during freshman year?

_____

_____

9-23. ***Are Best Actresses Younger than Best Actors?*** Listed below are ages of actresses and actors at the times that they won Oscars. The data are paired according to the years that they won. Use a 0.05 significance level to test the common belief that best actresses are younger than best actors. Does the result suggest a problem in our culture?

Best Actresses	28 32 27 27 26 24 25 29 41 40 27 42 33 21 35
Best Actors	62 41 52 41 34 40 56 41 39 49 48 56 42 62 29

Test statistic: _____   *P*–value: _____

Conclusion in your own words: _____

_____

9-24. ***Are Flights Cheaper When Scheduled Earlier?*** Listed below are the costs (in dollars) of flights from New York (JFK) to San Francisco for seven different airlines. Use a 0.01 significance level to test the claim that flights scheduled one day in advance cost more than flights scheduled 30 days in advance. What strategy appears to be effective in saving money when flying?

Flight scheduled one day in advance	456 614 628 1088 943 567 536
Flight scheduled 30 days in advance	244 260 264 264 278 318 280

Test statistic: _____   *P*–value: _____

Conclusion in your own words: _____

_____

9-25. ***Does Your Body Temperature Change During the Day?*** Listed below are body temperatures (in °F) of subjects measured at 8 AM and at 12 AM (from University of Maryland physicians listed in the "Body Temperatures" dataset in Appendix B). Construct a 95% confidence interval estimate of the difference between the 8 AM temperatures and the 12 AM temperatures. Is body temperature basically the same at both times?

8 AM	97.0 96.2 97.6 96.4 97.8 99.2
12 AM	98.0 98.6 98.8 98.0 98.6 97.6

Test statistic: _____   *P*–value: _____

Conclusion in your own words: _____

_____

9-26. ***Is Blood Pressure the Same for Both Arms?*** Listed below are systolic blood pressure measurements (mm Hg) taken from the right and left arms of the same woman (based on data from "Consistency of Blood Pressure Differences Between the Left and Right Arms," by Eguchi et al, *Archives of Internal Medicine*, Vol. 167). Use a 0.05 significance level to test for a difference between the measurements from the two arms. What do you conclude?

| Right arm | 102 | 101 | 94 | 79 | 79 |
| Left arm | 175 | 169 | 182 | 146 | 144 |

Test statistic: _____ *P*–value: _____

Conclusion in your own words: _____

_____

9-27. ***Appendix B Data Set: Paper or Plastic?*** Refer to the "Garbage Weight" dataset in Appendix B. Construct a 95% confidence interval estimate of the mean of the differences between weights of discarded paper and weights of discarded plastic. Which seems to weigh more: discarded paper or discarded plastic?

_____

_____

9-28. ***Appendix B Data Set: Glass and Food*** Refer to the "Garbage Weight" dataset in Appendix B. Construct a 95% confidence interval estimate of the mean of the differences between weights of discarded glass and weights of discarded food. Which seems to weigh more: discarded glass or discarded food?

_____

_____

9-29. ***Testing Effects of Alcohol*** Researchers conducted an experiment to test the effects of alcohol. The errors were recorded in a test of visual and motor skills for a treatment group of 22 people who drank ethanol and another group of 22 people given a placebo. The errors for the treatment group have a standard deviation of 2.20, and the errors for the placebo group have a standard deviation of 0.72 (based on data from "Effects of Alcohol Intoxication on Risk Taking, Strategy, and Error Rate in Visuomotor Performance," by Streufert, et al., *Journal of Applied Psychology,* Vol. 77, No. 4). Use a 0.05 significance level to test the claim that the treatment group has errors that vary more than the errors of the placebo group.

Test statistic: _____ *P*–value: _____

Conclusion in your own words: _____

_____

9-30. ***Heights*** Listed below are heights (cm) of randomly selected females and males taken from the data set "Body Data" in Appendix B. Use a 0.05 significance level to test the claim that females and males have heights with the same amount of variation.

Female	163.7	165.5	163.1	166.3	163.6	170.9	153.5	155.7	153.0	157.0
Male	178.8	177.5	187.8	172.4	181.7	169.0	186.9	183.1	176.4	183.4

Test statistic: _____   *P*–value: _____

Conclusion in your own words: _____

_____

9-31. ***Freshman 15 Study*** Use the sample weights (kg) of male and female college students measured in April of their freshman year, as listed in the "Freshman 15" dataset in Appendix B. Use a 0.05 significance level to test the claim that near the end of the freshman year, weights of male college students vary more than weights of female college students.

Test statistic: _____   *P*–value: _____

Conclusion in your own words: _____

_____

9-32. ***M&Ms*** Refer to the "M&M Weights" dataset in Appendix B and use the weights (g) of the red M&Ms and the orange M&Ms. Use a 0.05 significance level to test the claim that the two samples are from populations with the same amount of variation.

Test statistic: _____   *P*–value: _____

Conclusion in your own words: _____

_____

10

Correlation and Regression

10-1 Minitab's Assistant Feature

Minitab introduced its new *Assistant* feature in Release 16 and it is currently available. If you click on the main menu item of **Assistant,** you get a submenu that includes the option of **Regression.** If you click on Regression, you will get a screen that includes the following.

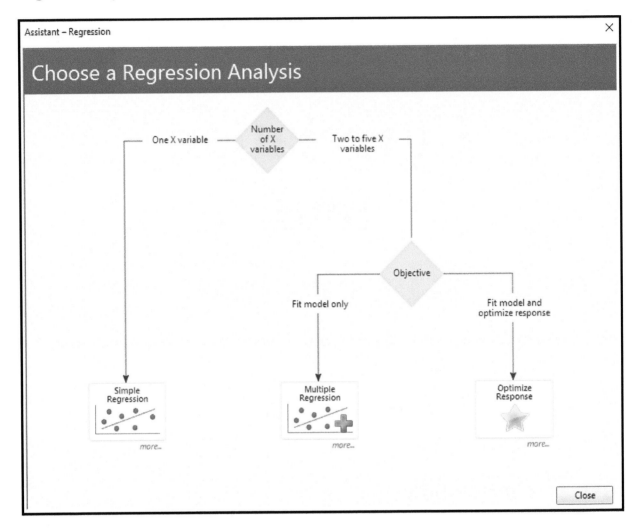

Clicking on the above box starts a process for an in-depth analysis of correlation and regression. You must enter the columns containing the lists of data to be used for the *x* and *y* variables, and results will be displayed in four different screens providing a wealth of information, including the linear correlation coefficient, *P*-value, scatterplot, equation of the regression line, a "report card" with comments about normality, unusual points, sample size, a diagnostic report that uses residuals, and a "model selection" report. The following sections of this manual/workbook describe the use of Minitab's basic functions, but consider using the *Assistant* feature in place of those basic methods.

10-2 Scatterplot

Chapter 10 in the Triola textbook introduces the basic concepts of linear correlation and regression. The basic objective is to use paired sample data to determine whether there is a relationship between two variables and, if so, identify what the relationship is. Consider the paired sample data in the table below. The data consist of measured shoe print lengths and heights of five males. We want to determine whether there is a relationship between shoe print length and height. If such a relationship exists, we want to identify it with an equation so that we can predict the height of a male based on the length of his shoe print.

Table 10-1 Shoe Print Lengths and Heights of Males

Shoe Print (cm)	29.7	29.7	31.4	31.8	27.6
Height (cm)	175.3	177.8	185.4	175.3	172.7

Before using concepts of correlation and regression, it is always wise to construct a scatterplot so that we can see if there appears to be a relationship between the two variables, and we can see if the pattern of points is approximately the pattern of a straight line. The Minitab procedure for constructing a scatterplot was given in Section 2-4 of this manual/workbook. Enter the paired data in columns of Minitab or open a Minitab worksheet, select **Graph**, then **Scatterplot**. Select the option of **Simple**, then click **OK**.

10-3 Correlation

The textbook describes the linear correlation coefficient r as a measure of the strength of the linear relationship between two variables. Minitab can compute the value of r for paired data. Instead of performing complicated manual calculations, follow these steps to let Minitab calculate r.

Minitab Procedure for Calculating the Linear Correlation Coefficient r

1. Enter the paired x and y values in individual columns (such as C1 and C2), or open a Minitab worksheet containing the columns of paired data. It is also wise to enter names of the variables in the empty cells located immediately above the first row of data values.

2. Select **Stat**, then **Basic Statistics**, then **Correlation**.

3. In the dialog box, enter the column labels (such as C1 C2), or enter the variable names, then click **OK**.

4. Confirm that for the "Method" box, **Pearson correlation** is selected, and also confirm that the "Display p-values" box is checked.

Shown below is the Minitab display that results from using the data in the above table. The variable names of ShoePrint and Height were also entered. Because the *P*-value of 0.294 is greater than the significance level of 0.05, we conclude that there is not sufficient evidence to support the claim of a linear correlation between the lengths of shoe prints and heights of males.

```
Correlation: ShoePrint, Height

Pearson correlation of ShoePrint and Height = 0.591
P-Value = 0.294
```

10-4 Regression

Section 10-2 in the textbook discusses the important topic of regression. Given a collection of paired sample data, the **regression equation**

$$\hat{y} = b_0 + b_1 x$$

describes the relationship between the two variables. The graph of the regression equation is called the **regression line** (or *line of best fit*, or *least-squares line*). The regression equation expresses a relationship between x (called the *independent variable* or *predictor variable*) and y (called the *dependent variable* or *response variable*). The y-intercept of the line is b_0 and the slope is b_1. Given a collection of paired data, we can find the regression equation as follows.

Minitab Procedure for Finding the Equation of the Regression Line

1.   Enter the paired x and y values in individual columns (such as C1 and C2), or open a Minitab worksheet containing the columns of paired data. It is also   wise to enter names of the variables in the empty cells located immediately above the first row of data values.

2.   Select **Stat, Regression, Fitted Line Plot.**

3.   Make these entries in the "Fitted Line Plot" dialog box:

- Enter the column name containing the y values in the box for "Response."

- Enter the column name containing the x values in the box for "Predictor."

- For the "Type of Regression Model," select **Linear.**

- Click **OK.**

Using the sample data in the preceding table, if you use the response variable of Height and the predictor variable of ShoePrint, the Minitab display will be as follows.

This display includes the regression equation, which we can express as $\hat{y} = 125 + 1.73x$ or as Height = 125 + 1.73ShoePrint. The Minitab display also includes "R-sq = 35.0%," which is the coefficient of determination defined in the textbook; that value indicates that 35.0% of the variation in heights can be explained by the linear correlation between shoe print lengths and heights, and 65.0% of the variation in heights remains unexplained. This display also includes a graph of the scatterplot with the regression line shown.

10-5 Predictions

Important: When making predictions, do not blindly substitute values into the regression equation. See Section 10-2 in the textbook, and see Figure 10-5 reproduced here.

Strategy for Predicting Values of *y*

Is the regression equation a good model?
- The regression line graphed in the scatterplot shows that the line fits the points well.
- *r* indicates that there is a linear correlation.
- The prediction is not much beyond the scope of the available sample data.

Yes.
The regression equation is a good model.

No.
The regression equation *is not* a good model.

Substitute the given value of *x* into the regression equation
$\hat{y} = b_0 + b_1 x$

Regardless of the value of *x*, the best predicted value of *y* is the value of $\overline{y}$ (the mean of the *y* values).

FIGURE 10-5   Recommended Strategy for Predicting Values of *y*

We can use Minitab for making predictions by letting Minitab substitute a value of *x* into the regression equation. We can also find prediction intervals, as described in Section 10-3 of the textbook. Use the following procedure, which is strange because it requires that you must first find a regression equation (using **Stat/Regression/Regression/Fit Regression Model**) before you can use the prediction feature (using **Stat/Regression/Regression/*Predict***). Here goes.

Minitab Procedure for Predictions and Prediction Intervals

1. Enter the paired *x* and *y* values in individual columns (such as C1 and C2), or open a Minitab worksheet containing the columns of paired data. It is also wise to enter the names of the variables in the empty cells located immediately above the first row of data values.

2. Select **Stat**, then **Regression, Regression,** then **Fit Regression Model.**

3.   Make these entries in the dialog box:

- Enter the column name containing the *y* values in the box for "Responses."

- Enter the column name containing the *x* values in the box for "Continuous predictors." ("Categorical predictors" would consist of categorical data.)

- Click **OK**.

4.   You should see results that include the equation of the regression line. Now select **Stat/Regression/Regression/*Predict.***

5.   In the dialog box that appears, the top "Response" box should include the column representing the *y* variable, and the second box gives you the option of "entering individual values" directly in the dialog box, or "entering a column" of *x* values to be used for predictions. Choose one of those options and make the required entries.

6.   Click on **Options** and select the confidence level to be used for constructing a prediction interval, as described in Section 10-3 of the textbook.

Example 1 in the textbook uses paired chocolate/Nobel data to find a 95% prediction interval based on a chocolate consumption amount of *x* = 10 kg per capita. Here is the Minitab result:

```
Prediction for Nobel
Regression Equation
Nobel = -3.37 + 2.493 Chocolate


Variable    Setting
Chocolate        10


    Fit    SE Fit         95% CI                  95% PI
21.5647   2.15029   (17.0929, 26.0364)    (7.79443, 35.3349)
```

Given *x* = 10, the best predicted value of *y* is 21.5647 or 21.6 rounded. The 95% prediction interval is 7.9 < *y* < 35.3 when rounded. If we select some country with a chocolate consumption rate of 10 kg per capita, we have 95% confidence that the limits of 7.8 and 35.3 contain the Nobel Laureate rate.

10-6 Multiple Regression

Section 10-4 in the textbook discusses multiple regression, and Minitab can provide multiple regression results. Once a collection of sample data has been entered, you can easily experiment with different combinations of columns (variables) to find the combination that is best. Here is the Minitab procedure.

Minitab Procedure for Multiple Regression

1. Enter the sample data in columns (such as C1, C2, C3, . . .) or open a Minitab worksheet containing the columns of sample data. Also enter the *names* of the variables in the empty cells located immediately above the first row of sample values.

2. Click on **Stat**, **Regression**, **Regression**, **Fit Regression Model**.

3. Make these entries in the dialog box:

    - Enter the column name containing the *y* values in the box for "Responses."

    - Enter the names of the columns in the "Continuous predictors" box. ("Categorical predictors" would consist of categorical data.)

    - Click **OK**.

Example As an example, the table below includes measurements obtained from anesthetized bears. If you enter the sample data included in the table and select column C1 as the response variable and columns C3 and C6 as predictor variables, the Minitab results will be as shown below the table. The results correspond to this multiple regression equation:

$$\hat{y} = -374 + 18.8x_3 + 5.87x_6$$
$$\text{or WEIGHT} = -374 + 18.8(\text{HEADLEN}) + 5.87(\text{Length})$$

The results also include the adjusted coefficient of determination (75.92%) as well as a *P*-value (0.012) for overall significance of the multiple regression equation.

Data from Anesthetized Male Bears

Var.	Minitab Column	Name	Sample Data							
y	C1	WEIGHT	80	344	416	348	262	360	332	34
x_2	C2	AGE	19	55	81	115	56	51	68	8
x_3	C3	HEADLEN	11.0	16.5	15.5	17.0	15.0	13.5	16.0	9.0
x_4	C4	HEADWDTH	5.5	9.0	8.0	10.0	7.5	8.0	9.0	4.5
x_5	C5	NECK	16.0	28.0	31.0	31.5	26.5	27.0	29.0	13.0
x_6	C6	LENGTH	53.0	67.5	72.0	72.0	73.5	68.5	73.0	37.0
x_7	C7	CHEST	26	45	54	49	41	49	44	19

10-7 Nonlinear Regression

Nonlinear regression is discussed in the Triola statistics textbooks (except *Essentials of Statistics*). The objective is to find a mathematical function that "fits" or describes real-world data. Among the models discussed in the textbook, we will describe how Minitab can be used for the linear, quadratic, logarithmic, exponential, and power models.

To illustrate the use of Minitab, consider the sample data in the table below. As in the textbook, we will use the coded year values for x, so that $x = 1, 2, 3, \ldots, 11$. The y values are the populations (in millions) of 5, 10, 17, ..., 281. For the following models, we enter the coded years 1, 2, 3, ..., 11 in column C1 and we enter 5, 10, 17, ..., 281 in column C2. The resulting models are based on the coded values of x (1, 2, 3, ..., 11) and the population values in millions (5, 10, 17, ..., 281).

Population (in millions) of the United States

Year	1800	1820	1840	1860	1880	1900	1920	1940	1960	1980	2000
Coded year	1	2	3	4	5	6	7	8	9	10	11
Population	5	10	17	31	50	76	106	132	179	227	281

Linear Model: $y = a + bx$

The linear model can be obtained by using **Stat/Regression/Fitted Line Plot** as described in Section 10-4 of this manual/workbook. For the data in the above table, enter the coded year values of 1, 2, 3, ..., 11 in column C1 and enter the population values of 5, 10, 17, ..., 281 in column C2. The result will be $y = -61.9 + 27.2x$ with $R^2 = 92.5\%$ (or 0.925). The high value of R^2 suggests that the linear model is a reasonably good fit.

Quadratic Model: $y = ax^2 + bx + c$

With the coded values of x in column C1 and the population values (in millions) in column C2, select **Stat**, **Regression**, **Fitted Line Plot**. In the dialog box, enter C2 for the response variable, enter C1 for the predictor variable, and click on the **Quadratic** option. The results show that the function has the form given as $y = 10.01 - 6.003x + 2.767x^2$ with $R^2 = 0.999$. This higher value of R^2 suggests that the quadratic model is a better fit than the linear model.

Logarithmic Model: $y = a + b \ln x$

Minitab does not have a direct procedure for finding a logarithmic model, but there are ways to get it. One approach is to replace the coded x values (1, 2, 3, ..., 11) with $\ln x$ values (ln 1, ln 2, ln 3, ..., ln 11) This can be accomplished by using the command editor in the session window; enter the command LET C1 = LOGE(C1). [You could also use **Calc/Calculator** with the expression LOGE(C1).] After replacing the x values with $\ln x$ values, use **Stat**, **Regression**, **Fitted Line Plot** as in Section 10-4. That is, use the same procedure for finding the linear regression equation. The result is $y = -65.89 + 105.1(\ln x)$, with $R^2 = 0.696$, suggesting that this model does not fit as well as the linear or quadratic models. Of the three models considered so far, the quadratic model appears to be best.

Exponential Model: $y = ab^x$

The exponential model is tricky, but it can be obtained using Minitab. Enter the values of x in the first column, and enter the values of ln y in the second column. The values of ln y can be found by using the command editor in the session window; enter the command LET C2 = LOGE(C2). [You could also use **Calc/Calculator** with the expression LOGE(C2).]

    After replacing the y values with ln y values, use **Stat**, **Regression**, **Fitted Line Plot** to find the linear regression equation as described in Section 10-4 of this book. When you get the results from Minitab, the value of the coefficient of determination is correct, but the values of a and b in the exponential model must be computed as follows:

    To find the value of a: Evaluate e^{b_0} where b_0 is the y-intercept given by Minitab.

    To find the value of b: Evaluate e^{b_1} where b_1 is the slope given by Minitab.

Using the data in the above table, the value of $R^2 = 0.963$ is OK as is, but Minitab's regression equation of $y = 1.6556 + 0.39405x$ must be converted as follows.

$$a = e^{b_0} = e^{1.6556} = 5.2362$$
$$b = e^{b_1} = e^{0.39405} = 1.4830$$

Using these values of a and b, we express the exponential model as $y = 5.2362(1.4830^x)$.

Power Model: $y = ax^b$

Replace the x values with ln x values and replace the y values with ln y values. The values of ln x can be found by using the command editor in the session window; enter the command LET C1 = LOGE(C1). [You could also use **Calc/Calculator** with the expression LOGE(C1).] The values of ln y can be found the same way. Then use **Stat**, **Regression**, **Fitted Line Plot** to find the linear regression equation as described in Section 10-4 of this workbook. When you get the results from Minitab, the value of the coefficient of determination is correct, the value of b is the same as the slope of the regression line, but the y-intercept must be converted as follows.

    To find the value of a: Evaluate e^{b_0} where b_0 is the y-intercept given by Minitab.

Using the data in the above table, we get $R^2 = 0.976$. From Minitab's linear regression equation of $y = 1.2099 + 1.76606x$, we get $b = 1.76606$ and a is computed as follows.

$$a = e^{b_0} = e^{1.2099} = 3.35315$$

Using these values of a and b, we express the power model as $y = 3.35315(x^{1.76606})$.

    The rationale underlying the methods for the exponential and power models is based on transformations of equations. In the exponential model of $y = ab^x$, for example, taking natural logarithms of both sides yields ln y = ln a + x (ln b), which is the equation of a straight line. Minitab can be used to find the equation of this straight line that fits the data best; the intercept will be ln a and the slope will be ln b, but we need the values of a and b, so we solve for them as described above. Similar reasoning is used with the power model.

CHAPTER 10 EXPERIMENTS: Correlation and Regression

10–1. ***Bear Weights and Ages*** Refer to the "Bear Measurements" dataset in Appendix B of the textbook . Use the values for WEIGHT (x) and the values for AGE (y) to find the following.

    a.   Display the scatter diagram of the paired WEIGHT/AGE data. Based on that scatter diagram, does there appear to be a relationship between the weights of bears and their ages? If so, what is it?

        _____

    b.   Find the value of the linear correlation coefficient r. _____

    c.   Assuming a 0.05 level of significance, what do you conclude about the correlation between weights and ages of bears?

        _____

    d.   Find the equation of the regression line. (Use WEIGHT as the x predictor variable, and use AGE as the y response variable.) _____

    e.   What is the best predicted age of a bear that weighs 300 lb?_____

10–2. ***Effect of Transforming Data*** The ages used in Experiment 10–1 are in months. Convert them to days by multiplying each age by 30, then repeat Experiment 10–1 and enter the responses here:

    a.   Display the scatter diagram of the paired WEIGHT/AGE data. Based on that scatter diagram, does there appear to be a relationship between the weights of bears and their ages? If so, what is it?

        _____

    b.   Find the value of the linear correlation coefficient r._____

    c.   Assuming a 0.05 level of significance, what do you conclude about the correlation between weights and ages of bears?

        _____

    d.   Find the equation of the regression line. (Use WEIGHT as the x predictor variable, and use AGE as the y response variable.) _____

    e.   What is the best predicted age of a bear that weighs 300 lb?_____

    f.   After comparing the responses obtained in Experiment 10-1 to those obtained here, describe the general effect of changing the scale for one of the variables.

        _____

        _____

10–3. ***Bear Weights and Chest Sizes*** Refer to the "Bear Measurements" dataset in Appendix B of the textbook. Use the values for CHEST (x) and the values for WEIGHT (y) to find the following.

    a.   Display the scatter diagram of the paired CHEST/WEIGHT data. Based on that scatter diagram, does there appear to be a relationship between the chest sizes of bears and their weights? If so, what is it?

             _____

    b.   Find the value of the linear correlation coefficient r. _____

    c.   Assuming a 0.05 level of significance, what do you conclude about the correlation between chest sizes and weights of bears?

             _____

    d.   Find the equation of the regression line. (Use CHEST as the x predictor variable, and use WEIGHT as the y response variable.) _____

    e.   What is the best predicted weight of a bear with a chest size of 36.0 in?_____

    f.   When trying to obtain measurements from an anesthetized bear, what is a practical advantage of being able to predict the bear's weight by using its chest size?

             _____

             _____

10–4. ***Effect of No Variation for a Variable*** Use the following paired data and obtain the indicated results.

x	1	2	3	4	5	7	7	9
y	5	5	5	5	5	5	5	5

    a.   Print a scatter diagram of the paired x and y data. Based on the result, does there appear to be a relationship between x and y? If so, what is it?

             _____

    b.   What happens when you try to find the value of r? Why?

             _____

    c.   What do you conclude about the correlation between x and y? What is the equation of the regression line?

             _____

10–5. *Town Courts* Listed below are amounts of court income and salaries paid to the town justices (based on data from the *Poughkeepsie Journal*). All amounts are in thousands of dollars, and all of the towns are in Dutchess County, New York.

Court Income	65	404	1567	1131	272	252	111	154	32
Justice Salary	30	44	92	56	46	61	25	26	18

Is there a correlation between court incomes and justice salaries? Explain.

_____

What is the equation of the regression line? _____

Find the best predicted justice salary for a court with income of \$83,941 (or \$83.941 thousand). _____

10–6. *Car Repair Costs* Listed below are repair costs (in dollars) for cars crashed at 6 mi/h in full-front crash tests and the same cars crashed at 6 mi/h in full-rear crash tests (based on data from the Insurance Institute for Highway Safety). The cars are the Toyota Camry, Mazda 6, Volvo S40, Saturn Aura, Subaru Legacy, Hyundai Sonata, and Honda Accord.

Front	936	978	2252	1032	3911	4312	3469
Rear	1480	1202	802	3191	1122	739	2767

Is there a correlation between front and rear repair costs? Explain.

_____

What is the equation of the regression line? _____

Find the best predicted repair cost for a full-rear crash for a Volkswagon Passat, given that its repair cost from a full-front crash is \$4594. _____

10–7. *Movie Data* Refer to the data from movies in the table below, where all amounts are in millions of dollars. Let the movie gross amount be the dependent *y* variable.

Budget	62	90	50	35	200	100	90
Gross	65	64	48	57	601	146	47

Is there a correlation between the budget amount and the gross amount? Explain.

_____

What is the equation of the regression line? _____

Find the best predicted gross amount for a movie with a budget of \$150 million._____

10–8. *Crickets and Temperature* The numbers of chirps in one minute were recorded for different crickets, and the corresponding temperatures were also recorded. The results are given in the table below.

Chirps in one minute	882	1188	1104	864	1200	1032	960	900
Temperature (°F)	69.7	93.3	84.3	76.3	88.6	82.6	71.6	79.6

Is there a correlation between the number of chirps and the temperature? Explain.

_____

What is the equation of the regression line? _____

Find the best predicted temperature when a cricket chirps 1000 times in one minute.___

10–9. *Blood Pressure*   Refer to the systolic and diastolic blood pressure measurements from randomly selected subjects. Let the dependent variable y represent diastolic blood pressure.

Systolic	138	130	135	140	120	125	120	130	130	144	143	140	130	150
Diastolic	82	91	100	100	80	90	80	80	80	98	105	85	70	100

Is there a correlation between systolic and diastolic blood pressure? Explain.

_____

What is the equation of the regression line? _____

Find the best predicted measurement of diastolic blood pressure for a person with a systolic blood pressure of 123. _____

10–10. *Garbage Data for Predicting Household Size* The "Garbage Weight" dataset in Appendix B of the textbook consists of data from the Garbage Project at the University of Arizona. Use household size (HHSIZE) as the response y variable. For each predictor x variable given below, find the value of the linear correlation coefficient, the equation of the regression line, and the value of the coefficient of determination r^2. Enter the results in the spaces below.

(continued)

	r	Equation of regression line	r^2
Metal	___	_____	___
Paper	___	_____	___
Plastic	___	_____	___
Glass	___	_____	___
Food	___	_____	___
Yard	___	_____	___
Text	___	_____	___
Other	___	_____	___
Total	___	_____	___

Based on the above results, which single independent variable appears to be the best predictor of household size? Why?

_____

_____

10–11. Use the same data set described in Experiment 10-10. Let household size (HHSIZE) be the dependent y variable and use the given predictor x variables to fill in the results below.

	Multiple regression eq.	R^2	Adj. R^2
Metal and Paper	_____	___	_____
Plastic and Food	_____	___	_____
Metal, Paper, Glass	_____	___	_____
Metal, Paper, Plastic, Glass	_____ _	___	_____

Based on the above results, which of the multiple regression equations appears to best fit the data? Why?

_____

_____

10-12. ***Appendix B Data Set: Predicting Nicotine in Cigarettes*** Refer to the "Cigarette Contents" dataset in Appendix B and use the tar, nicotine, and CO amounts for the cigarettes that are 100 mm long, filtered, non-menthol, and non-light (the last set of measurements). Find the best regression equation for predicting the amount of nicotine in a cigarette. Is the best regression equation a good regression equation for predicting the nicotine content?

_____

_____

_____

10-13. ***Predicting IQ Score*** Refer to the "IQ and Brain Size" dataset in Appendix B and find the best regression equation with IQ score as the response (y) variable. Use predictor variables of brain volume and/or weight. Why is this equation best? Based on these results, can we predict someone's IQ score if we know the volume and weight of their brain? Based on these results, does it appear that people with larger brains have higher IQ scores?

_____

_____

_____

10-14. ***Full IQ Score*** Refer to the "IQ and Lead" dataset in Appendix B and find the best regression equation with IQF (full IQ score) as the response (y) variable. Use predictor variables of IQV (verbal IQ score) and IQP (performance IQ score). Why is this equation best? Based on these results, can we predict someone's full IQ score if we know their verbal IQ score and their performance IQ score? Is such a prediction likely to be very accurate?

_____

_____

_____

10-15. *Manatee Deaths from Boats* Listed below are the numbers of Florida manatee deaths related to encounters with watercraft (based on data from *The New York Times*). The data are listed in order, beginning with the year 1980 and ending with the year 2000.

16 24 20 15 34 33 33 39 43 50 47 53 38 35 49 42 60 54 67 82 78

Use the given data to find equations and coefficients of determination for the indicated models.

	Equation	R^2
Linear	_____	_____
Quadratic	_____	_____
Logarithmic	_____	_____
Exponential	_____	_____
Power	_____	_____

Based on the above results, which model appears to best fit the data? Why?

_____

_____

What is the best predicted value for 2001? In 2001, there were 82 watercraft–related manatee deaths. How does the predicted value compare to the actual value?

_____

_____

_____

11

Goodness-of-Fit and Contingency Tables

11-1 Goodness-of-Fit

We use a *goodness-of-fit* test with sample data consisting of observed frequency counts arranged in a single row or column (called a one-way frequency table). We test for the claim that the observed frequency counts agree with some claimed distribution, so that there is a *good fit* of the observed data with the claimed distribution.

Minitab Procedure for Goodness-of-Fit

1. First collect the observed values O and enter them in column C1.

2. If the expected frequencies are not all the same, enter the expected *proportions* in column C2.

3. Select **Stat**, **Tables**, and **Chi-Square Goodness-of-Fit Test (One Variable).**

4. Enter C1 in the "Observed counts" box.

5. Select "Equal proportions" if the expected frequencies are all the same. Otherwise, select "Specific proportions" and enter C2 in the box.

6. Click **OK.**

As an example, consider the following table listing the frequency counts of the 100 last digits of the weights of Californians. We want to test the claim that the observed digits are from a population of weights in which the last digits do not occur with the same frequency.

Last Digits of Weights

Last Digit	Frequency
0	46
1	1
2	2
3	3
4	3
5	30
6	4
7	0
8	8
9	3

After entering the observed frequencies column C1, select **Stat, Tables,** select **Chi-Square Goodness-of-Fit Test (One Variable)** and use the dialog box as shown below.

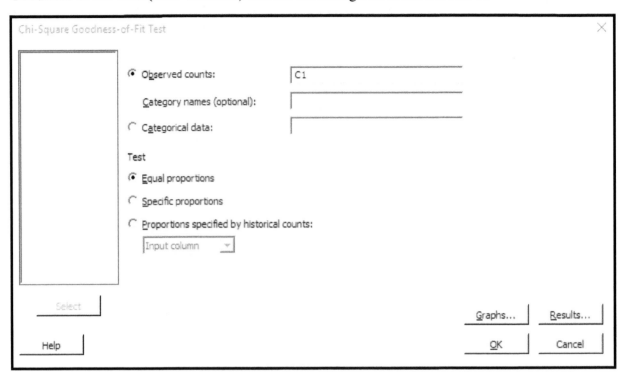

The Minitab results are shown below. The *P*-value of 0.000 suggests that we reject the null hypothesis that the digits occur with the same frequency. There is sufficient evidence to support the claim that the digits do *not* occur with the same frequency.

Chi-Square Goodness-of-Fit Test for Observed Counts in Variable: C1

Category	Observed	Test Proportion	Expected	Contribution to Chi-Sq
1	46	0.1	10	129.6
2	1	0.1	10	8.1
3	2	0.1	10	6.4
4	3	0.1	10	4.9
5	3	0.1	10	4.9
6	30	0.1	10	40.0
7	4	0.1	10	3.6
8	0	0.1	10	10.0
9	8	0.1	10	0.4
10	3	0.1	10	4.9

N	DF	Chi-Sq	P-Value
100	9	212.8	0.000

11-2 Contingency Tables

A **contingency table** (or **two-way frequency table**) is a table in which frequencies correspond to two variables. One variable is used to categorize rows, and a second variable is used to categorize columns. Let's consider the data in the contingency table shown below.

Study of Success with Different Treatments for Stress Fracture

	Success	Failure
Surgery	54	12
Weight-Bearing Cast	41	51
Non-Weight Bearing Cast for 6 Weeks	70	3
Non-Weight Bearing Cast Less than 6 Weeks	17	5

To use Minitab with a contingency table, follow this procedure:

Minitab Procedure for Contingency Tables

1. Enter the individual columns of data in Minitab columns C1, C2, C3, . . . , .
    The Minitab display shows the data from the above table.

2. Select **Stat, Tables, Chisquare Test for Association**.

3. In the top box select **Summarized data in a two-way table.** Proceed to enter the names of the columns containing the observed frequencies. For the above data, enter C1 C2. Click **OK**.

Shown below are the Minitab results from the data in the above table. The *P*-value of 0.000 is less than a 0.05 significance level, so we reject the null hypothesis of independence between the row and column variables. It appears that success or failure is dependent on the treatment.

Chi-Square Test for Association: Worksheet rows, Worksheet columns

```
Rows: Worksheet rows    Columns: Worksheet columns

            C1      C2   All

1           54      12    66
         47.48   18.52

2           41      51    92
         66.18   25.82

3           70       3    73
         52.51   20.49

4           17       5    22
         15.83    6.17

All        182      71   253

Cell Contents:       Count
                     Expected count


Pearson Chi-Square = 58.393, DF = 3, P-Value = 0.000
Likelihood Ratio Chi-Square = 62.691, DF = 3, P-Value = 0.000
```

CHAPTER 11: Goodness-of-Fit and Contingency Tables

11-1. ***Loaded Die*** The author drilled a hole in a die and filled it with a lead weight, then proceeded to roll it 200 times. Here are the observed frequencies for the outcomes of 1, 2, 3, 4, 5, and 6 respectively: 27, 31, 42, 40, 28, 32. Use a 0.05 significance level to test the claim that the outcomes are not equally likely.

Test statistic:_____   *P*-value:_____

Conclusion:_____

_____

Does it appear that the loaded die behaves differently than a fair die?

_____

11-2. ***Flat Tire and Missed Class*** A classic tale involves four car-pooling students who missed a test and gave as an excuse a flat tire. On the makeup test, the instructor asked the students to identify the particular tire that went flat. If they really didn't have a flat tire, would they be able to identify the same tire? The author asked 41 other students to identify the tire they would select. The results are listed in the following table (except for one student who selected the spare). Use a 0.05 significance level to test the author's claim that the results fit a uniform distribution.

Tire	Left front	Right front	Left rear	Right rear
Number selected	11	15	8	6

Test statistic:_____   *P*-value:_____

Conclusion:_____

_____

What does the result suggest about the ability of the four students to select the same tire when they really didn't have a flat?

_____

11-3. ***Births*** Records of randomly selected births were obtained and categorized according to the day of the week that they occurred (based on data from the National Center for Health Statistics). Because babies are unfamiliar with our schedule of weekdays, a reasonable claim is that births occur on the different days with equal frequency. Use a 0.01 significance level to test that claim.

Day	Sun	Mon	Tues	Wed	Thurs	Fri	Sat
Births	77	110	124	122	120	123	97

Test statistic:_____   *P*-value:_____

Conclusion:_____

_____

11-4. ***NYC Homicides*** For a recent year, the following are the numbers of homicides that occurred each month in New York City: 38, 30, 46, 40, 46, 49, 47, 50, 50, 42, 37, 37. Use a 0.05 significance level to test the claim that homicides in New York City are equally likely for each of the 12 months.

Test statistic:_____   *P*-value:_____

Conclusion:_____

_____

11–5. ***Measuring Pulse Rates*** According to one procedure used for analyzing data, when certain quantities are measured, the last digits tend to be uniformly distributed, but if they are estimated or reported, the last digits tend to have disproportionately more 0s or 5s. Refer to the "Body Data" dataset in Appendix B of the textbook and use the last digits of the pulse rates of the men and women (combined). Those pulse rates were obtained as part of the National Health and Examination Survey. Test the claim that the last digits of 0, 1, 2, 3, . . . , 9 occur with the same frequency.

Test statistic:_____   *P*-value:_____

Conclusion:_____

_____

What can be inferred about the procedure used to obtain the pulse rates?

_____

11-6. ***Testing a Normal Distribution*** In this experiment we will use Minitab's ability to generate normally distributed random numbers. We will then test the sample data to determine if they actually do fit a normal distribution.

a. Generate 1000 random numbers from a normal distribution with a mean of 100 and a standard deviation of 15. (IQ scores have these parameters.) Select **Calc**, then **Random Data**, then **Normal**.

b. Use **Data/Sort** to arrange the data in order.

c. Examine the sorted list and determine the frequency for each of the categories listed below. Enter those frequencies in the spaces provided. (The expected frequencies are found by assuming that the data are normally distributed.)

	Observed Frequency	**Expected Frequency**
Below 55:	_____	1
55-70:	_____	22
70-85:	_____	136
85-100:	_____	341
100-115:	_____	341
115-130:	_____	136
130-145:	_____	22
Above 145:	_____	1

d. Use Minitab to test the claim that the randomly generated numbers actually do fit a normal distribution with mean 100 and standard deviation 15.

Test statistic:_____   *P*-value:_____

Conclusion:_____

_____

11-7. ***Instant Replay in Tennis*** The table below summarizes challenges made by tennis players in the first U. S. Open that used the Hawk-Eye electronic instant replay system. Use a 0.05 significance level to test the claim that success in challenges is independent of the gender of the player. Does either gender appear to be more successful?

	Was the challenge to the call successful?	
	Yes	No
Men	201	288
Women	126	224

Test statistic:_____   *P*-value:_____

Conclusion:_____

_____

11–8. ***Accuracy of Polygraph Tests*** The data in the accompanying table summarize results from tests of the accuracy of polygraphs (based on data from the Office of Technology Assessment). Use a 0.05 significance level to test the claim that whether the subject lies is independent of the polygraph indication.

	Polygraph Indicated Truth	Polygraph Indicated Lie
Subject actually told the truth	65	15
Subject actually told a lie	3	17

Test statistic:_____   *P*-value:_____

Conclusion:_____

_____

What do the results suggest about the effectiveness of polygraphs?

_____

_____

11–9. *Global Warming Survey* A Pew Research poll was conducted to investigate opinions about global warming. The respondents who answered yes when asked if there is solid evidence that the earth is getting warmer were then asked to select a cause of global warming. The results are given the table below. Use a 0.05 significance level to test the claim that the sex of the respondent is independent of the choice for the cause of global warming. Do men and women appear to agree, or is there a substantial difference?

	Human activity	Natural patterns	Don't know or refused to answer
Male	314	146	44
Female	308	162	46

Test statistic:_____   *P*-value:_____

Conclusion:_____

_____

11–10. *Occupational Hazards* Use the data in the table to test the claim that occupation is independent of whether the cause of death was homicide. The table is based on data from the U.S. Department of Labor, Bureau of Labor Statistics.

	Police	Cashiers	Taxi Drivers	Guards
Homicide	82	107	70	59
Cause of Death Other than Homicide	92	9	29	42

Test statistic:_____   *P*-value:_____

Conclusion:_____

_____

Does any particular occupation appear to be most prone to homicides? If so, which one?

_____

How are the results affected if the order of the rows is switched?

_____

How are the results affected by the presence of an outlier? If we change the first entry from 82 to 8200, are the results dramatically affected?

_____

12

Analysis of Variance

12-1 One-Way Analysis of Variance

One–way analysis of variance is used to test the claim that three or more populations have the same mean. When the Triola textbook discusses one-way analysis of variance, it is noted that the term "one-way" is used because the sample data are separated into groups according to one characteristic or "factor." In Table 12-1 the factor is the blood lead level (low, medium, high).

Table 12-1 Performance IQ Scores of Children

Low Blood Lead Level

```
 85   90 107   85  100 97  101  64  111 100   76  136 100   90 135 104 149 99  107 99
113  104 101  111  118 99  122  87  118 113  128  121 111  104  51 100 113 82  146 107
 83  108  93  114  113 94  106  92   79 129  114   99 110   90  85  94 127 101  99 113
 80  115  85  112  112 92   97  97   91 105   84   95 108  118 118  86  89 100
```

Medium Blood Lead Level

```
 78  97  107  80  90   83  101  121 108  100 110
111  97   51  94  80  101   92  100  77  108  85
```

High Blood Lead Level

```
93  100  97  79  97  71  111  99  85  99  97  111  104  93  90  107  108  78  95  78  86
```

Because the calculations are very complicated, the Triola textbook emphasizes the interpretation of results obtained by using software, so Minitab is very suitable for this topic. We should understand that a small P-value (such as 0.05 or less) leads to rejection of the null hypothesis of equal means. ["If the P (value) is low, the null must go."] With a large P-value (such as greater than 0.05), fail to reject the null hypothesis of equal means.

For the data in the above table, the claim of equal means leads to these hypotheses:

$H_0: \mu_1 = \mu_2 = \mu_3$

H_1: At least one of the population means is different from the others.

With Minitab Release 16 or later, you could use the new "Assistant" feature by clicking on the main menu item of **Assistant.** Select **Hypothesis Tests,** then select **One-Way ANOVA.** Use of the Assistant feature yields four screens of results that include much helpful information. The following procedure describes another way that Minitab can be used to test the claim that the different samples come from populations with the same mean.

Minitab Procedure for One-Way Analysis of Variance

1.   Enter the original sample values in columns (or open a Minitab worksheet that contains the columns of data).

2.   Select **Stat** from the main menu.

3.   Select the subdirectory item of **ANOVA**.

4.   In the top box, select the option of **Response data are in a separate column for each factor level.** (The other option can be used if all of the sample data are in one column and there is another column that describes the factor.)

5.   In the second box, enter the column names (such as C1 C2 C3) in the box labeled as "Responses." Click **OK**.

If you use the above steps with the performance IQ scores from the above table, the Minitab results will appear as shown below. (There are additional results not shown here.)

One-way ANOVA: IQ PERF_1, IQ PERF_2, IQ PERF_3

Method

Null hypothesis	All means are equal
Alternative hypothesis	At least one mean is different
Significance level	$\alpha = 0.05$

Equal variances were assumed for the analysis.

Factor Information

Factor	Levels	Values
Factor	3	IQ PERF_1, IQ PERF_2, IQ PERF_3

Analysis of Variance

Source	DF	Adj SS	Adj MS	F-Value	P-Value
Factor	2	2023	1011.4	4.07	0.020
Error	118	29314	248.4		
Total	120	31337			

The *P*-value of 0.020 indicates that there is sufficient sample evidence to warrant rejection of the null hypothesis that $\mu_1 = \mu_2 = \mu_3$. The test statistic of $F = 4.07$ is also provided.

The lower portion of the preceding Minitab display is not shown here, but it includes 95% confidence interval estimates of each of the three population means. These confidence intervals are computed by the same methods used in Chapter 7, except that a pooled standard deviation is used instead of the individual sample standard deviations. Not shown here is the last entry in the Minitab display showing that the pooled standard deviation is 15.7615.

12-2 Two-Way Analysis of Variance

Two-way analysis of variance involves *two* factors, such as gender (male or female) and blood lead level (low, medium, high) in the table shown below. The two–way analysis of variance procedure requires that we (1) test for an interaction effect between the two factors; (2) test for an effect from the row factor; (3) test for an effect from the column factor.

Measures of Performance IQ			
	Blood Lead Level		
	Low	Medium	High
Male	85	78	93
	90	107	97
	107	90	79
	85	83	97
	100	101	111
Female	64	97	100
	111	80	71
	76	108	99
	136	110	85
	99	97	93

Entering the Sample Data The first obstacle to overcome is to understand a somewhat awkward method of entering sample data. When entering the values in the above table, we must somehow keep track of the location of each data value, so here is the procedure to be used:

1.   Enter *all* of the sample data in column C1.

2.   Enter the corresponding row numbers in column C2.

3.   Enter the corresponding column numbers in column C3.

This particular format can be confusing at first, so stop and try to recognize the pattern. Because the first value of 85 from the above table is in the first row and first column, its row identification is 1 and its column identification is 1. The entry of 90 is also in the first row and first column, so its row identification number is 1 and its column identification number is 1. (The sample values of 85, 90, 107, 85, 100 are all considered to be in the first row (male) and the first column (low). The value of 78 is in the first row and second column.

    Also, it's wise to name column C1 as "IQ," name column C2 as "GENDER", and name column C3 "LEAD" so that the columns have meaningful names. The following illustration shows the pattern used to enter the sample data in the above table. The Minitab display includes only the first 12 values from Table 12-3.

Table 12-3	Measures of Performance IQ		
	Blood Lead Level		
	Low	**Medium**	**High**
Male	85	78	93
	90	107	97
	107	90	79
	85	83	97
	100	101	111
Female	64	97	100
	111	80	71
	76	108	99
	136	110	85
	99	97	93

IQ	GENDER	LEAD
85	1	1
90	1	1
107	1	1
85	1	1
100	1	1
64	2	1
111	2	1
76	2	1
136	2	1
99	2	1
78	1	2
107	1	2

The procedure for obtaining a Minitab display for two-way analysis of variance is as follows. (*Caution:* Minitab's procedure for two-way analysis of variance in Release 16 included a simple procedure that was made considerably more complicated in Release 17.)

Minitab Procedure for Two-Way Analysis of Variance

1.   Enter all of the sample values in column C1 (as shown above).

2.   Enter the corresponding row numbers in column C2 (as shown above).

3.   Enter the corresponding column numbers in column C3 (as shown above).

4.   Select **Stat**, then **ANOVA, General Linear Model,** then **Fit General Linear Model.**

5.   You should now see a dialog box like the one shown below.

      Make these entries in the dialog box:

      •   Enter C1 (or its column label) in the box labeled Response.

      •   Enter C2 (or its column label) in the box labeled Row Factor.

      •   Enter C3 (or its column label) in the box labeled Column Factor.

6.　　Click the **Model** button.

7.　　Under *Factors and Covariates,* use the mouse to highlight C2 and C3 (or the names of the columns) as shown in the display below, then click the **Add** button. In the box named "Terms in the model," you should see C1*C2 or in this case, GENDER*LEAD, which is telling Minitab to include interaction results.

8.　　Click **OK** twice.

Using the performance IQ data in the preceding table will result in the Minitab display shown below.

```
Analysis of Variance

Source        DF   Adj SS   Adj MS  | F-Value   P-Value
   GENDER      1    17.63    17.63  |   0.07     0.791
   LEAD        2    48.80    24.40  |   0.10     0.906
   GENDER*LEAD 2   211.47   105.73  |   0.43     0.655
Error         24  5886.40   245.27  |_____
Total         29  6164.30
```

The Triola textbooks (excluding *Essentials of Statistics*) describe the interpretation of the preceding Minitab display.

1. Test for Interaction

We begin by testing the null hypothesis that there is no *interaction* between the two factors of GENDER and LEAD. Using the above Minitab results, we calculate the following test statistic.

$$F = \frac{\text{MS(interaction)}}{\text{MS(error)}} = \frac{105.73}{245.27} = 0.43$$

Interpretation: The corresponding *P*-value is shown in the Minitab display as 0.655, so we fail to reject the null hypothesis of no interaction between the two factors. It does not appear that the performance IQ scores are affected by an interaction between gender (male, female) and blood lead level (low, medium, high). There does not appear to be an interaction effect.

2. Test for Effect from the Row Factor

Our two-way analysis of variance procedure outlined in the textbook indicates that we should now proceed to test these two null hypotheses: (1) There are no effects from the row factor of GENDER; (2) There are no effects from the column factor of LEAD. For the test of an effect from the row factor of GENDER, we have the following:

$$F = \frac{MS(\text{sex})}{MS(\text{error})} = \frac{17.633}{245.267} = 0.07$$

Conclusion: The corresponding *P*-value is shown in the Minitab display as 0.791. Because that *P*-value is greater than the significance level of 0.05, we fail to reject the null hypothesis of no effects from sex. That is, performance IQ scores do not appear to be affected by the sex of the subject.

3. Test for Effect from the Column Factor
For the test of an effect from SIZE, we have

$$F = \frac{MS(\text{lead level})}{MS(\text{error})} = \frac{24.40}{245.27} = 0.10$$

Conclusion: The corresponding *P*-value is shown in the Minitab display as 0.906. Because that *P*-value is greater than the significance level of 0.05, we fail to reject the null hypothesis of no effects from lead level. Performance IQ scores do not appear to be affected by whether the lead exposure is low, medium, or high.

CHAPTER 12 EXPERIMENTS: Analysis of Variance

12-1. ***Clancy, Rowling, Tolstoy Readability*** Pages were randomly selected by the author from *The Bear and the Dragon* by Tom Clancy, *Harry Potter and the Sorcerer's Stone* by J. K. Rowling, and *War and Peace* by Leo Tolstoy. The Flesch Reading Ease scores for those pages are listed below. Use a 0.05 significance level to test the claim that the three samples are from populations with the same mean. Do the books appear to have different reading levels of difficulty?

Clancy	58.2	73.4	73.1	64.4	72.7	89.2	43.9	76.3	76.4	78.9	69.4	72.9
Rowling	85.3	84.3	79.5	82.5	80.2	84.6	79.2	70.9	78.6	86.2	74.0	83.7
Tolstoy	69.4	64.2	71.4	71.6	68.5	51.9	72.2	74.4	52.8	58.4	65.4	73.6

SS(treatment): _____ MS(treatment): _____ Test statistic F: _____

SS(error): _____ MS(error): _____ P-value: _____

SS(total): _____

Conclusion:_____

_____

12-2. ***Poplar Tree Weights*** Weights (kg) of poplar trees were obtained from trees planted in a sandy and dry region. The trees were given different treatments identified in the table below. The data are from a study conducted by researchers at Pennsylvania State University, and the data were provided by Minitab, Inc. Use a 0.05 significance level to test the claim that the four treatment categories yield poplar trees with the same mean weight. Is there a treatment that appears to be most effective in the sandy and dry region?

No Treatment	Fertilizer	Irrigation	Fertilizer and Irrigation
1.21	0.94	0.07	0.85
0.57	0.87	0.66	1.78
0.56	0.46	0.10	1.47
0.13	0.58	0.82	2.25
1.30	1.03	0.94	1.64

SS(treatment): _____ MS(treatment): _____ Test statistic F: _____

SS(error): _____ MS(error): _____ P-value: _____

SS(total): _____

Conclusion:_____

12–3. *Archeology: Skull Breadths from Different Epochs*   The values in the table are measured maximum breadths of male Egyptian skulls from different epochs (based on data from Ancient Races of the Thebaid, by Thomson and Randall-Maciver). Changes in head shape over time suggest that interbreeding occurred with immigrant populations. Use a 0.05 significance level to test the claim that the different epochs do not all have the same mean.

4000 B.C.	1850 B.C.	150 A.D.
131	129	128
138	134	138
125	136	136
129	137	139
132	137	141
135	129	142
132	136	137
134	138	145
138	134	137

SS(treatment): _____   MS(treatment): _____   Test statistic F: _____

SS(error): _____   MS(error): _____ P-value: _____

SS(total): _____

Conclusion:_____

12–4. *Mean Weights of M&Ms*   Refer to the dataset "M&M Weights" in Appendix B from the textbook. At the 0.05 significance level, test the claim that the mean weight of M&Ms is the same for each of the six different color populations.

SS(treatment): _____   MS(treatment): _____   Test statistic F: _____

SS(error): _____   MS(error): _____ P-value: _____

SS(total): _____

Conclusion:_____

If it is the intent of Mars, Inc., to make the candies so that the different color populations have the same mean weight, do these results suggest that the company has a problem requiring corrective action?

12–5. *Nicotine in Cigarettes* Refer to the "Cigarette Contents" dataset in Appendix B and use the amounts of nicotine (mg per cigarette) in the king size cigarettes, the 100 mm menthol cigarettes, and the 100 mm non-menthol cigarettes. The king size cigarettes are non-filtered, non-menthol, and non-light. The 100 mm menthol cigarettes are filtered and non-light. The 100 mm non-menthol cigarettes are filtered and non-light. Use a 0.05 significance level to test the claim that the three categories of cigarettes yield the same mean amount of nicotine. Given that only the king size cigarettes are not filtered, do the filters appear to make a difference?

SS(treatment): _____   MS(treatment): _____   Test statistic *F*: _____

SS(error): _____   MS(error): _____   *P*-value: _____

SS(total): _____

Conclusion:_____

12–6. *Tar in Cigarettes* Refer to the "Cigarette Contents" dataset in Appendix B and use the amounts of tar (mg per cigarette) in the three categories of cigarettes described in Experiment 12-5. Use a 0.05 significance level to test the claim that the three categories of cigarettes yield the same mean amount of tar. Given that only the king size cigarettes are not filtered, do the filters appear to make a difference?

SS(treatment): _____   MS(treatment): _____   Test statistic *F*: _____

SS(error): _____   MS(error): _____   *P*-value: _____

SS(total): _____

Conclusion:_____

12-7. *Simulations* Use Minitab to randomly generate three different samples of 500 values each. (Select **Calc, Random Data, Normal**.) For the first two samples, use a normal distribution with a mean of 100 and a standard deviation of 15. For the third sample, use a normal distribution with a mean of 105 and a standard deviation of 15. We know that the three populations have different means, but do the methods of analysis of variance allow you to conclude that the means are different? Explain.

_____

_____

_____

12–8. *Pulse Rates* The following table lists pulse rates obtained from the "Body Data" dataset in Appendix B of the textbook. Use a 0.05 significance level and apply the methods of two-way analysis of variance. What do you conclude?

	Under 30 Years of Age	Over 30 Years of Age
Female	78 104 78 64 60 98 82 98 90 96	76 76 72 66 72 78 62 72 74 56
Male	60 80 56 68 68 74 74 68 62 56	46 70 62 66 90 80 60 58 64 60

Are pulse rates affected by an interaction between gender and age? Explain.

_____

Are pulse rates affected by gender? Explain.

_____

Are pulse rates affected by age? Explain.

_____

_____

12-9. *Smoking, Body Temperature, Gender* The table below lists body temperatures obtained from randomly selected subjects (based on the "Body Temperatures" dataset in Appendix B). The temperatures are categorized according to gender and whether the subject smokes. Using a 0.05 significance level, test for an interaction between gender and smoking, test for an effect from gender, and test for an effect from smoking. What do you conclude?

	Smokes	Does not smoke
Male	8.4 98.4 99.4 98.6	98.0 98.0 98.8 97.0
Female	8.8 98.0 98.7 98.4	97.7 98.0 98.2 99.1

Are body temperatures affected by an interaction between sex and smoking? Explain.

_____

Are body temperatures affected by sex? Explain.

_____

Are body temperatures affected by smoking? Explain.

_____

_____

13

Nonparametric Tests

13-1 Ranking Data

This chapter describes how Minitab can be used for the nonparametric methods presented in the Triola textbook. The sections of this chapter correspond to those in the textbook. The textbook introduces some basic principles of nonparametric methods, but it also describes a procedure for converting data into their corresponding *ranks*. Here is the Minitab procedure for using data in column C1 to create a column C2 that consists of the corresponding ranks.

Converting Data to Ranks

1. Enter the data values in column C1.

2. Select **Data** from the main menu.

3. Select **Rank** from the subdirectory.

4. In the dialog box, make these entries:

   - For the box labeled "Rank data in," enter C1.

   - For the box labeled "Store ranks in," enter C2.

   - Click **OK**.

As an example, enter the values of 5, 3, 40, 10, 12, and 12 in column C1, follow the above steps, and column C2 will contain the ranks of 2, 1, 6, 3, 4.5, and 4.5 as shown below.

C1	C2
Data	Ranks
5	2.0
3	1.0
40	6.0
10	3.0
12	4.5
12	4.5

Ties: Note that Minitab handles ties as described in the Triola textbook. See the above display that includes ties in the ranks that correspond to the values of 12 and 12. Ties occur with the corresponding ranks of 4 and 5, so Minitab assigns a rank of 4.5 to each of those values.

13-2 Sign Test

The Triola textbook (excluding *Essentials of Statistics*) includes a description of the sign test in Section 13-2.

Definition
The **sign test** is a nonparametric (distribution-free) test that uses plus and minus signs to test different claims, including:
1. Claims involving matched pairs of sample data
2. Claims involving nominal data with two categories
3. Claims about the median of a single population

Sign Test With Matched Data Minitab makes it possible to work with all three of the above cases. Let's consider the matched data in the table below. (The data are matched, because each pair of values is from the same flight.)

Taxi-Out Times and Taxi-In Times for American Airlines Flight 21

Taxi-out time	13	20	12	17	35	19	22	43	49	45	13	23
Taxi-in time	13	4	6	21	29	5	27	9	12	7	36	12
Sign of difference	0	+	+	−	+	+	−	+	+	+	−	+

Given such paired data, we can use Minitab to apply the sign test to test the claim of no difference.

Minitab Procedure for Sign Test with Matched Data

    1. Enter the values of the first variable in column C1.

    2. Enter the values of the second variable in column C2.

    3. Create column C3 equal to the values of C1 − C2. Accomplish this using either of the following two approaches.

        Session window: Click on the session window at the top portion of the screen, then click on **Editor**, then click on **Enable Commands**. Enter the command:
        LET C3 = C1 − C2.

        Calculator: Click on **Calc**, then **Calculator**. In Minitab's calculator, enter C3 for the "Store result in variable" box, and enter the expression C1 − C2 in the "expression" box. Click **OK** when done.

4. Select **Stat** from the main menu.

5. Select **Nonparametrics** from the subdirectory.

6. Select the option of **1-Sample Sign**.

7. Make these entries in the resulting dialog box:

- For the box labeled Variables, enter C3 (which contains the differences obtained when column C2 is subtracted from column C1).

- Click on the button for **Test median** and, in the adjacent box, enter 0 for a test of the claim that the median is equal to zero.

- In the box labeled Alternative, select **not equal,** so that the alternative hypothesis is that the statement that the median is not equal to zero.

- Click **Ok**.

Here are the Minitab results for the data in the above table:

```
Sign test of median =  0.00000 versus ≠ 0.00000

      N  Below  Equal  Above      P  Median
C3   12      3      1      8  0.2266   8.500
```

The above results show that there are 12 pairs of data, there are 3 differences that are below zero (negative sign), one of the differences is equal to zero, and 8 of the differences are above zero (positive sign). The P-value is 0.2266. In the textbook, we would use a decision criterion that involves a comparison of the test statistic $x = 3$ (the less frequent sign) and a critical value found in Table A-7. Because Minitab displays the P-value, we can use the P-value approach to hypothesis testing. Because the P-value of 0.2266 is greater than the significance level of $\alpha = 0.05$, there is not sufficient evidence to warrant rejection of the claim that the median of the differences is equal to 0. There does not appear to be significant difference between the taxi-out times and the taxi-in times.

Sign Test With Nominal Data   A test of a gender-selection method resulted in 945 babies, including 879 girls and 66 boys. Because the data are at the nominal level of measurement, we could enter them as −1's (for girls) and 1's (for boys). *Shortcut*: Instead of entering −1 a total of 879 times and 1 a total of 66 times, we can enter the following commands in the session window to achieve the same result. (Click on the session window at the top portion of the screen, then click on **Editor**, then click on **Enable Commands**. Enter these commands to create a column consisting of −1 repeated 879 times and 1 repeated 66 times.)

```
SET C3
879(-1), 66(1)
END
```

Now follow the procedure given earlier (beginning with step 3) for conducting the sign test, and the results will be as shown below.

```
Sign test of median =  0.00000 versus ≠ 0.00000

        N   Below   Equal   Above        P   Median
C3    945     879       0      66   0.0000   -1.000
```

The resulting *P*-value of 0.0000 suggests that we reject the null hypothesis of equality of girls and boys. There is sufficient evidence to warrant rejection of the claim that girls and boys are equally likely.

Sign Test for Testing a Claimed Value of the Median   We can apply the sign test to test a claim about the *median* of a set of data values. For example, open the "Body Temperatures" dataset from Appendix B and use the 106 values in the last column. We will test the claim that the mean body temperature is less than 98.6°. Follow the procedure for doing the sign test, but make these changes in the dialog box entries of Step 6: Enter 98.6 in the box adjacent to "Test median," and select "less than" in the box labeled Alternative. The Minitab results will be as shown below.

```
Sign test of median = 98.60 versus   <  98.60

                   N   Below   Equal   Above        P   Median
Day 2 - 12 AM    106      68      15      23   0.0000    98.40
```

The above Minitab display shows that among the 106 body temperatures, 68 are below 98.6, 15 are equal to 98.6, and 23 are above 98.6. The *P*-value of 0.0000 causes us to reject the null hypothesis that the median is at least 98.6. There appears to be sufficient evidence to support the claim that the median body temperature is less than 98.6° F.

13-3 Wilcoxon Signed-Ranks Test

The Triola textbook (excluding *Essentials of Statistics*) describes the Wilcoxon signed-ranks test.

Definition

The **Wilcoxon signed-ranks test** is a nonparametric test that uses ranks for these applications:

1. Testing a claim that the population of matched pairs has the property that the matched pairs have differences with median equal to zero

2. Testing a claim that a single population of individual values has median equal to some claimed value

---

The textbook makes this important point: The Wilcoxon signed-ranks test and the sign test can both be used with sample data consisting of matched pairs, but the sign test uses only the *signs* of the differences and not their actual magnitudes (how large the numbers are). The Wilcoxon signed-ranks test uses *ranks*, so the magnitudes of the differences are taken into account. Because the Wilcoxon signed-ranks test incorporates and uses more information than the sign test, it tends to yield conclusions that better reflect the true nature of the data. First we describe the Minitab procedure for conducting a Wilcoxon signed-ranks test, then we illustrate it with an example.

Minitab Procedure for the Wilcoxon Signed-Ranks Test

     1. Enter the values of the first variable in column C1.

     2. Enter the values of the second variable in column C2.

     3. Create column C3 equal to the values of C1 − C2. Accomplish this using either of the following two approaches.

        Session window: Click on the session window at the top portion of the screen, then click on **Editor**, then click on **Enable Commands**. Enter the command:
        LET C3 = C1 − C2.

        Calculator: Click on **Calc**, then **Calculator**. In Minitab's calculator, enter C3 for the "Store result in variable" box, and enter the expression C1 − C2 in the "expression" box. Click **OK** when done.

     4. Select **Stat** from the main menu.

     5. Select **Nonparametrics** from the subdirectory.

(continued)

6. Select the option of **1-Sample Wilcoxon**.

7. Make these entries in the resulting dialog box:

- **Variables:** For the box labeled Variables, enter C3 (which contains the differences obtained when column C2 is subtracted from column C1).

- **Test Median:** Click on the button for "Test median," and in the adjacent box, enter 0 for a test of the claim that the median is equal to zero.

- **Alternative:** In the box labeled Alternative, select "not equal" for a test of the claim that the median is equal to zero (so that the alternative hypothesis is that the median is not equal to zero).

- Click **OK**.

Using the same matched data from the table in Section 13-2 of this manual/workbook), the Minitab results for the Wilcoxon signed-ranks test will be as shown below.

Wilcoxon Signed Rank Test: C3

Test of median = 0.000000 versus median $\neq$ 0.000000

	N	N for Test	Wilcoxon Statistic	P	Estimated Median
C3	12	11	55.0	0.056	10.00

From these results we see that the *P*-value is 0.056. Because the *P*-value of 0.056 is greater than the significance level of 0.05, we fail to reject the null hypothesis that the matched pairs have differences with a median equal to 0. There does not appear to be a significant difference between the taxi-in times and the corresponding taxi-out times.

13-4 Wilcoxon Rank-Sum Test

The Triola textbook (excluding *Essentials of Statistics*) discusses the Wilcoxon rank-sum test.

Definition

The **Wilcoxon rank-sum test** is a nonparametric test that uses ranks of sample data from two independent populations to test this null hypothesis:

H_0: The two independent samples come from populations with equal medians.

(The alternative hypothesis H_1 can be any one of the following three possibilities: The two populations have different medians, or the first population has a median *greater than* the median of the second population, or the first population has a median *less than* the median of the second population.)

The Wilcoxon rank-sum test described in the textbook is equivalent to the Mann-Whitney U test, so use Minitab's Mann-Whitney procedure for testing the claim that two independent samples come from populations with populations with equal medians.

Minitab Procedure for the Mann-Whitney Test
(Equivalent to the Wilcoxon Rank-Sum Test)

1. Enter the two sets of sample data in columns C1 and C2.

2. Select **Stat** from the main menu.

3. Select **Nonparametrics**.

4. Select **Mann-Whitney**.

5. Make these entries in the dialog box:

   - Enter C1 for the first sample and enter C2 for the second sample.

   - Enter the confidence level in the indicated box. (A confidence level of 95.0 corresponds to a significance level of $\alpha = 0.05$.)

   - Select the desired form of the alternative hypothesis.

Shown below are pulse rates of males and females (from the "Body Temperatures" dataset in Appendix B). Ranks are shown in parentheses. We want to use a 0.05 significance level to test the claim that males and females have the same median pulse rate. Also shown are the Minitab results that include a *P*-value of 0.2166. Based on the available sample data, it appears that there is not sufficient evidence to warrant rejection of the claim that males and females have pulse rates with the same median.

Table 13-5 Pulse Rates

(Ranks in parentheses)

Males	Females
60 (**4.5**)	78 (**14**)
74 (**11**)	80 (**17**)
86 (**19**)	68 (**9**)
54 (**1**)	56 (**2.5**)
90 (**20.5**)	76 (**12**)
80 (**17**)	78 (**14**)
66 (**7**)	78 (**14**)
68 (**9**)	90 (**20.5**)
68 (**9**)	96 (**22**)
56 (**2.5**)	60 (**4.5**)
80 (**17**)	98 (**23**)
62 (**6**)	
$n_1 = 12$	$n_2 = 11$
$R_1 = 123.5$	$R_2 = 152.5$

Mann-Whitney Test and CI: Males, Females

```
          N   Median
Males    12    68.00
Females  11    78.00


Point estimate for ETA1-ETA2 is -10.00
95.5 Percent CI for ETA1-ETA2 is (-20.00,4.01)
W = 123.5
Test of ETA1 = ETA2 vs ETA1 not = ETA2 is significant at
0.2184
The test is significant at 0.2166 (adjusted for ties)
```

13-5 Kruskal-Wallis Test

The Triola textbook (excluding *Essentials of Statistics*) discusses the Kruskal-Wallis test.

Definition

The **Kruskal-Wallis Test** (also called the ***H* test**) is a nonparametric test that uses ranks of simple random samples from three or more independent populations to test the null hypothesis that the populations have the same median. (The alternative hypothesis is the claim that the populations have medians that are not all equal.)

Caution: Using Minitab for a Kruskal-Wallis test is somewhat tricky, because we must enter all of the data in *one column*, then enter the corresponding identifiers in another column. For an example, see the sample data in the table below left, and see the format required by Minitab at the right. The columns at the right show only the first 10 data values, but all of the data must be listed with the same pattern.

Performance IQ Scores

Low Lead Level	Medium Lead Level	High Lead Level
85	78	93
90	97	100
107	107	97
85	80	79
100	90	97
97	83	
101		
64		

Stacked Data

85	Low
90	Low
107	Low
85	Low
100	Low
97	Low
101	Low
64	Low
78	Medium
97	Medium

Stacking Data If the data are listed in separate columns and you want to stack them as shown above, use **Data/Stack** to combine them into one single column. After selecting **Data/Stack**, you will get a "Stack Columns" dialog box. Enter the columns to be stacked, identify the column where the stacked data will be listed, and identify the column where the corresponding "subscripts" (identifiers) will be listed.

After the sample data have been arranged in a single column with identifiers in another column, we can proceed to use Minitab as follows.

Procedure for the Kruskal-Wallis Test

1. Enter the data values for all categories in one column, and enter the corresponding identification numbers or names in another column.

2. Select **Stat** from the main menu.

3. Select **Nonparametrics**.

4. Select **Kruskal-Wallis**.

5. Make these entries in the dialog box:

   - **Response:** For Response, enter the column with all of the sample data combined.

   - **Factor:** For Factor, enter the column of identification numbers or names.

   - Click **OK**.

Here are the Minitab results obtained by using the Kruskal-Wallis test with the data in the preceding table:

```
Kruskal-Wallis Test: IQ versus Lead

Kruskal-Wallis Test on IQ

Lead       N   Median   Ave Rank      Z
High       5    97.00       10.7   0.32
Low        8    93.50       10.8   0.50
Medium     6    86.50        8.4  -0.83
Overall   19                 10.0

H = 0.69  DF = 2  P = 0.707
H = 0.70  DF = 2  P = 0.704   (adjusted for ties)
```

Important elements of the Minitab display include the test statistic of $H = 0.70$ and the P–value of 0.704. We fail to reject the null hypothesis (the samples come from populations with the same median) only if the P–value is small (such as 0.05 or less). Assuming a 0.05 significance level in this case, we fail to reject the null hypothesis of equal medians. The population medians do not appear to be different.

13-6 Rank Correlation

The Triola textbook introduces *rank correlation*, which uses ranks in a procedure for determining whether there is some relationship between two variables.

Definition
The **rank correlation test** (or **Spearman's rank correlation test**) is a nonparametric test that uses ranks of sample data consisting of matched pairs. It is used to test for an association between two variables.

Minitab Procedure for Rank Correlation

   1. Enter the paired data in columns C1 and C2.

   2. Select **Stat** from the main menu.

   3. Select **Basic Statistics**.

   4. Select **Correlation**.

   5. In the top "Variables" box, enter C1 C2.

   6. For the "Method" box, select **Spearman rho.**

   7. Click on the box next to **Display p-values.**

Consider the sample data in the table below.

Overall Quality Scores and Prices of LCD Televisions

Quality Rank	1	2	3	4	5	6	7
Price (dollars)	1900	1200	1300	2000	1700	1400	2700

Using these data with the Minitab procedure for rank correlation, we obtain the following Minitab results showing that $r_s = 0.429$ and the *P*-value is 0.429. There is not sufficient evidence to support a claim of a correlation between quality and price.

```
Spearman Rho: C1, C2

Spearman rho for C9 and C10 = 0.429
P-Value = 0.337
```

13-7 Runs Test for Randomness

The Triola textbook (excluding *Essentials of Statistics*) discusses the runs test for randomness.

Definitions

After characterizing each data value as one of two separate categories, a **run** is a sequence of data having the same characteristic; the sequence is preceded and followed by data with a different characteristic or by no data at all.

The **runs test** uses the number of runs in a sequence of sample data to test for randomness in the order of the data.

When listing sequences of data to be used for the runs test, the textbook uses both numerical data and qualitative data, but Minitab works with *numerical* data only, so enter such a sequence using numbers instead of letters. As an illustration, consider the winners of the NBA basketball championship game, with W denoting a winner from the Western Conference and E denoting a winner from the Eastern Conference. We get the following sequence of E's and W's, which we then convert to 0's and 1's as shown below.

E	E	W	W	W	W	W	E	W	E	W	E	W	W	W
0	0	1	1	1	1	1	0	1	0	1	0	1	1	1

Minitab Procedure for the Runs Test for Randomness

1. In column C1, enter the sequence of *numerical* data. (If the sequence of data consists of two qualitative characteristics, represent the sequence using 0's and 1's.)

2. Select **Stat** from the main menu.

3. Select **Nonparametrics**.

4. Select **Runs** Test.

5. Make these entries in the dialog box:

   - Enter C1 in the box for variables.

   - Click on the button for **Above and below**, and enter a number in the adjacent box. (Choose a number appropriate for the test. If using 0's and 1's, enter 0.5.)

   - Click **OK**.

Consider the sequence of 107 genders of subjects as listed in the "Body Temperatures" dataset in Appendix B of the textbook. We want to use a 0.05 significance level to test the claim that the sequence of genders is random. After denoting each M by the number 1 and denoted each F by the number 0, we get a column of 107 numbers. The runs test results are as shown below (based on testing for randomness above and below 0.5).

Runs Test: Gender

```
Runs test for Gender

Runs above and below K = 0.5

The observed number of runs = 25
The expected number of runs = 26.7944
92 observations above K, 15 below
P-value = 0.465
```

The above results show that the P-value is 0.465, there are 25 runs, there are 92 values above 0.5 (or 92 males), and there are 15 values below 0.5 (or 15 females). Because the P-value is greater than the significance level of 0.05, we fail to reject the null hypothesis of randomness.

CHAPTER 13 EXPERIMENTS: Nonparametric Statistics

In Experiments 13–1 through 13–5, use Minitab's **sign test** *program.*

13-1. *Oscar Winners* Listed below are ages of actresses and actors at the times that they won Oscars. The data are paired according to the years that they won. Use a 0.05 significance level to test the claim that there is no difference between the ages of best actresses and the ages of best actors at the time that the awards were presented.

Best Actresses	33	35	35	28	30	29	61	32	33	45
Best Actors	36	47	29	43	37	38	45	50	48	60

P–value: _____

Conclusion: _____

_____

13-2. *Oscar Winners* Repeat the preceding exercise using all pairs of ages listed in the "Oscar Winner Age" dataset in Appendix B of the textbook.

P–value: _____

Conclusion: _____

_____

13-3. *Gender Selection* The Genetics and IVF Institute conducted a clinical trial of its methods for gender selection. As of this writing, 239 of 291 babies born to parents using the YSORT method were boys. Use a 0.01 significance level to test the claim that the YSORT method has no effect.

P–value: _____

Conclusion: _____

_____

13-4. *Earthquake Magnitudes* Refer to the "Earthquakes" dataset in Appendix B for the earthquake magnitudes. Use a 0.01 significance level to test the claim that the median is equal to 1.00.

P–value: _____

Conclusion: _____

_____

13-5. ***Testing for Median Weight of Quarters*** Refer to the "Coin Weights" dataset in Appendix B for the weights (in g) of randomly selected quarters that were minted after 1964. The quarters are supposed to have a median weight of 5.670 g. Use a 0.01 significance level to test the claim that the median is equal to 5.670 g. Do quarters appear to be minted according to specifications?

P–value: _____

Conclusion: _____

_____

***Experiments 13–6 through 13–10, involve the* Wilcoxon signed-ranks test.**

13–6. ***Sign Test vs. Wilcoxon Signed–Ranks Test*** Repeat Experiment 13-1 by using the Wilcoxon signed-ranks test for matched pairs. Enter the Minitab results below, and compare them to the sign test results obtained in Experiment 13-1. Specifically, how do the results reflect the fact that the Wilcoxon signed-ranks test uses more information?

P–value: _____

Conclusion: _____

_____

Comparison: _____

_____

13–7. ***Sign Test vs. Wilcoxon Signed–Ranks Test*** Repeat Experiment 13-2 by using the Wilcoxon signed-ranks test for matched pairs. Enter the Minitab results below, and compare them to the sign test results obtained in Experiment 13-2. Specifically, how do the results reflect the fact that the Wilcoxon signed-ranks test uses more information?

P–value: _____

Conclusion: _____

_____

Comparison: _____

_____

13–8. *Sign Test vs. Wilcoxon Signed–Ranks Test*   Repeat Experiment 13-4 by using the Wilcoxon signed-ranks test for matched pairs. Enter the Minitab results below, and compare them to the sign test results obtained in Experiment 13-4. Specifically, how do the results reflect the fact that the Wilcoxon signed-ranks test uses more information?

P–value: _____

Conclusion: _____

Comparison: _____

_____

13-9. *Earthquakes*   Refer to the "Earthquakes" dataset in Appendix B for the sample of paired earthquake magnitudes and depths. Use a 0.10 significance level with the Wilcoxon signed-ranks test to test the claim of no difference between the magnitudes and the depths.

P–value: _____

Conclusion: _____

_____

What is fundamentally wrong with this analysis?

_____

13-10. *Coke Contents*   Refer to the "Cola Weights and Volumes" dataset in Appendix B for the amounts (in oz) in cans of regular Coke. The cans are labeled to indicate that the contents are 12 oz of Coke. Use a 0.05 significance level with the Wilcoxon signed-ranks test to test the claim that cans of Coke are filled so that the median amount is 12 oz.

P–value: _____

Conclusion: _____

_____

*In Experiments 13–11 through 13–14, use the **Wilcoxon rank-sum test.***
(Minitab's Mann-Witney test procedure is equivalent to the Wilcoxon rank-sum test.)

13-11. *IQ and Lead Exposure* The "IQ and Lead" dataset in Appendix B lists full IQ scores for a random sample of subjects with medium lead levels in their blood and another random sample of subjects with high lead levels in their blood. Use a 0.05 significance level with the Wilcoxon rank-sum test to test the claim that subjects with medium lead levels have full IQ scores with a higher median than the median full IQ score for subjects with high lead levels.

P–value: _____

Conclusion: _____

13-12. *Weights of Coke* The "Cola Weights and Volumes" dataset in Appendix B lists weights (lb) of the cola in cans of regular Coke and diet Coke. Use a 0.05 significance level with the Wilcoxon rank-sum test to test the claim that the samples are from populations with the same median.

P–value: _____

Conclusion: _____

_____

13-13. *Cigarettes*   Refer to the "Cigarette Contents" dataset in Appendix B for the amounts of nicotine (in mg per cigarette) in the sample of king size cigarettes, which are non-filtered, non-menthol, and non-light, and for the amounts of nicotine in the 100 mm cigarettes, which are filtered, non-menthol, and non-light. Use a 0.01 significance level with the Wilcoxon rank-sum test to test the claim that the median amount of nicotine in the non-filtered king size cigarettes is greater than the median amount of nicotine in the 100 mm filtered cigarettes.

P–value: _____

Conclusion: _____

_____

13-14. ***Cigarettes*** Refer to the "Cigarette Contents" dataset in Appendix B for the amounts of tar in the sample of king size cigarettes, which are non-filtered, non-menthol, and non-light, and for to the amounts of tar in the 100 mm cigarettes, which are filtered, non-menthol, and non-light. Use a 0.01 significance level with the Wilcoxon rank-sum test to test the claim that the median amount of tar in the non-filtered king size cigarettes is greater than the median amount of tar in the 100 mm filtered cigarettes.

P–value: _____

Conclusion: _____

_____

***In Experiments 13–15 through 13–19, use the* Kruskal-Wallis test.**

13–15. ***Do All Colors of M&Ms Weigh the Same?*** Refer to the "M&M Weights" dataset in Appendix B from the textbook. Use a 0.05 significance level with the Kruskal-Wallis test to test the claim that the weights of M&Ms have the same median for each of the six different color populations.

P–value: _____

Conclusion: _____

_____

13-16. ***Nicotine in Cigarettes*** Refer to the "Cigarette Contents" dataset in Appendix B and use the amounts of nicotine (mg per cigarette) in the king size cigarettes, the 100 mm menthol cigarettes, and the 100 mm non-menthol cigarettes. The king size cigarettes are non-filtered, non-menthol, and non-light. The 100 mm menthol cigarettes are filtered and non-light. The 100 mm non-menthol cigarettes are filtered and non-light. Use a 0.05 significance level with the Kruskal-Wallis test to test the claim that the three categories of cigarettes yield the same median amount of nicotine.

P–value: _____

Conclusion: _____

_____

13-17. ***Tar in Cigarettes*** Refer to the "Cigarette Contents" dataset in Appendix B and use the amounts of tar (mg per cigarette) in the three categories of cigarettes described in the preceding exercise. Use a 0.05 significance level with the Kruskal-Wallis test to test the claim that the three categories of cigarettes yield the same median amount of tar.

P–value: _____

Conclusion: _____

_____

13-18. ***Carbon Monoxide from Cigarettes*** Refer to the "Cigarette Contents" dataset in Appendix B and use the amounts of carbon monoxide (mg per cigarette) in the three categories of cigarettes described in Exercise 16. Use a 0.05 significance level with the Kruskal-Wallis test to test the claim that the three categories of cigarettes yield the same median amount of carbon monoxide.

P–value: _____

Conclusion: _____

_____

13-19. ***Passive and Active Smoke*** The "Passive and Active Smoke" dataset in Appendix B of the textbook includes measured cotinine levels from a sample of subjects who smoke, another sample of subjects who do not smoke but are exposed to environmental tobacco smoke, and a third sample of subjects who do not smoke and are not exposed to environmental tobacco smoke. Cotinine is produced when the body absorbs nicotine. Use a 0.01 significance level to test the claim that the three samples are from populations with the same median.

P–value: _____

Conclusion: _____

_____

Experiments 13–20 through 13–25 involve **rank correlation.**

13-20. ***Judges of Marching Bands*** Two judges ranked seven bands in the Texas state finals competition of marching bands (Coppell, Keller, Grapevine, Dickinson, Poteet, Fossil Ridge, Heritage), and their rankings are listed below (based on data from the University Interscholastic League). Test for a correlation between the two judges. Do the judges appear to rank about the same or are they very different?

Band	Cpl	Klr	Grp	Dck	Ptt	FR	Her
First Judge	1	3	4	7	5	6	2
Second Judge	6	4	5	1	3	2	7

Rank Correlation Coefficient: _____

P–value: _____

Conclusion: _____

_____

13-21. ***Judges of Marching Bands*** In the same competition described in the preceding experiment, a third judge ranked the bands with the results shown below. Test for a correlation between the first and third judges. Do the judges appear to rank about the same or are they very different?

Band	Cpl	Klr	Grp	Dck	Ptt	FR	Her
First Judge	1	3	4	7	5	6	2
Third Judge	3	4	1	5	7	6	2

Rank Correlation Coefficient: _____

P–value: _____

Conclusion: _____

_____

13-22. **Blood Pressure** Refer to the measured systolic and diastolic blood pressure measurements of the males in the "Body Data" dataset in Appendix B of the textbook and test the claim that among males, there is a correlation between systolic blood pressure and diastolic blood pressure.

Rank Correlation Coefficient: _____

P–value: _____

Conclusion: _____

_____

13-23. **Blood Pressure** Refer to the measured systolic and diastolic blood pressure measurements of the females in the "Body Data" dataset in Appendix B of the textbook and test the claim that among females, there is a correlation between systolic blood pressure and diastolic blood pressure.

Rank Correlation Coefficient: _____

P–value: _____

Conclusion: _____

_____

13-24. **IQ and Brain Volume** Refer to the "IQ and Brain Size" dataset in Appendix B of the textbook and test the claim that there is a correlation between brain volume and IQ socre.

Rank Correlation Coefficient: _____

P–value: _____

Conclusion: _____

_____

13-25. *Earthquakes* Refer to the "Earthquakes" dataset in Appendix B of the textbook and test the claim that there is a correlation between magnitudes and depths of earthquakes.

Rank Correlation Coefficient: _____

P–value: _____

Conclusion: _____

_____

Experiments 13–26 through 13–29 involve the **runs test for randomness.**

13-26. *Oscar Winners* Listed below are the genders of the younger winner in the Academy Awards categories of Best Actor and Best Actress for recent and consecutive years. Do the genders of the younger winners appear to occur randomly?

F F F M M F F F F F M F F F M F F F

P–value: _____

Conclusion: _____

13-27. *Testing for Randomness of Presidential Election Winners* The political parties of the winning candidates for a recent sequence of presidential elections are listed below, where D denotes Democratic party and R denotes Republican party. Does it appear that we elect Democrat and Republican candidates in a random sequence?

R R D R D R R R R D D R R R D D D
D D R R D D R R D R R R D D R R D

P–value: _____

Conclusion: _____

13-28. ***Baseball World Series Victories*** Test the claim that the sequence of World Series wins by American League and National League teams is random. Given below are recent results, with American League and National League teams represented by A and N, respectively.

```
A N A N N N A A A A N A A A A N A N N A A N N A
A A A N A N N A A A A A N A N A N A N A A A A A
A A N N A N A N N A A N N A N A N A N A A A N
N A A N N N N A A A N A N A N A A A N A N A A A
N A N A A N A N A N N N A N
```

P–value: _____

Conclusion: _____

13-29. ***Stock Market*** Listed below are the annual high values of the Dow Jones Industrial Average for a recent sequence of years. Test for randomness below and above the median.

969	995	943	985	969	842	951	1036
1052	892	882	1015	1000	908	898	1000
1024	1071	1287	1287	1553	1956	2722	2184
2791	3000	3169	3413	3794	3978	5216	6561
8259	9374	11568	11401	11350	10635	10454	10855
10941	12464	14198	13279	10580	11625	12929	13589
16577	18054						

P–value: _____

Conclusion: _____

14

Statistical Process Control

14-1 Run Charts

In the Statistical Process Control chapter (Chapter 14) in the Triola textbook (excluding *Essentials of Statistics*) we define **process data** to be data arranged according to some time sequence, such as the data in the table below. This table lists measured weights of quarters produced with a new minting process. On each of 20 consecutive days of production, a quarter is selected during each of the first five hours of production and the quarter is weighed, and the results are listed in the table.

Weights (grams) of Minted Quarters

Day	Hour 1	Hour 2	Hour 3	Hour 4	Hour 5	$\bar{x}$	s	Range
1	5.543	5.698	5.605	5.653	5.668	5.6334	0.0607	0.155
2	5.585	5.692	5.771	5.718	5.720	5.6972	0.0689	0.186
3	5.752	5.636	5.660	5.680	5.565	5.6586	0.0679	0.187
4	5.697	5.613	5.575	5.615	5.646	5.6292	0.0455	0.122
5	5.630	5.770	5.713	5.649	5.650	5.6824	0.0581	0.140
6	5.807	5.647	5.756	5.677	5.761	5.7296	0.0657	0.160
7	5.686	5.691	5.715	5.748	5.688	5.7056	0.0264	0.062
8	5.681	5.699	5.767	5.736	5.752	5.7270	0.0361	0.086
9	5.552	5.659	5.770	5.594	5.607	5.6364	0.0839	0.218
10	5.818	5.655	5.660	5.662	5.700	5.6990	0.0689	0.163
11	5.693	5.692	5.625	5.750	5.757	5.7034	0.0535	0.132
12	5.637	5.628	5.646	5.667	5.603	5.6362	0.0235	0.064
13	5.634	5.778	5.638	5.689	5.702	5.6882	0.0586	0.144
14	5.664	5.655	5.727	5.637	5.667	5.6700	0.0339	0.090
15	5.664	5.695	5.677	5.689	5.757	5.6964	0.0359	0.093
16	5.707	5.890	5.598	5.724	5.635	5.7108	0.1127	0.292
17	5.697	5.593	5.780	5.745	5.470	5.6570	0.1260	0.310
18	6.002	5.898	5.669	5.957	5.583	5.8218	0.1850	0.419
19	6.017	5.613	5.596	5.534	5.795	5.7110	0.1968	0.483
20	5.671	6.223	5.621	5.783	5.787	5.8170	0.2380	0.602

A *run chart* is a sequential plot of *individual* data values over time. A run chart can be generated as follows.

Minitab Procedure for Generating a Run Chart

1. Enter all of the data (in sequence) in column C1.

2. Select the main menu item of **Stat**.

3. Select the subdirectory item of **Quality Tools**.

4. Select the option of **Run Chart**.

5. Make these entries in the dialog box:

   • Select **Single column** and enter C1 in the adjacent box.

   • Enter 1 for the subgroup size (because we want *individual* values plotted).

   • Click **OK**.

Using the process data in the preceding table, the above procedure will result in this run chart:

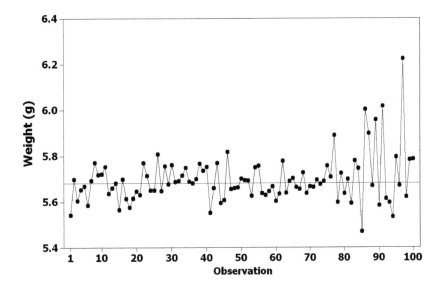

Examine the above run chart and note that it reveals this problem: As time progresses from left to right, the heights of the points appear to show a pattern of increasing *variation*. See how the points at the left fluctuate considerably less than the points farther to the right. It appears that the manufacturing process started out well, but deteriorated as time passed. If left alone, this minting process will continue to deteriorate because the run chart suggests that the process is not **statistically stable** (or **within statistical control**) because it has a pattern of increasing variation.

14-2 *R* Charts

The textbook describes *R* charts as sequential plots of ranges. Using the data from the preceding table, for example, the *R* chart is a plot of the ranges 0.155, 0.186, 0.187, . . . , 0.602. *R* charts are used to monitor the *variation* of a process. The procedure for obtaining an *R* chart is as follows.

Minitab Procedure for Creating *R* Charts

1. Enter all of the data in sequential order in column C1.

2. Select **Stat** from the main menu.

3. Select **Control Charts,** then select **Variable Charts for Subgroups**.

4. Select the option of **R**.

5. Make these entries in the dialog box:

   • Enter C1 in the box for the column containing all observations.

   • Enter a subgroup size of 5 in the indicated box. (We use 5 here because the preceding table of weights includes 5 observations each day.)

   • Click the **R options** button, click on the Estimate tab, then click on the button labeled **Rbar**. Click **OK** twice.

Using the data in the preceding table, the Minitab display will be as shown below.

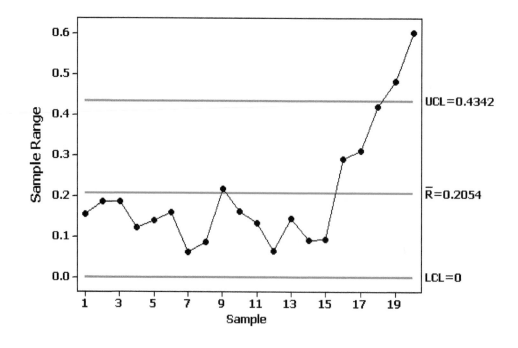

We can interpret the above R chart by applying these three criteria for determining whether a process is within statistical control:

1. There is no pattern, trend, or cycle that is obviously not random.

2. No point lies beyond the upper or lower control limits.

3. There are not 8 consecutive points all above or all below the center line.

Analyzing the above R chart leads to the conclusion that the process *is out of statistical control* because the second criterion is violated: There is a point beyond the upper control limit. Also, the third criterion is violated because there is a pattern of an upward trend, indicating that the process is experiencing increasing variation.

14-3 $\bar{x}$ Charts

We can now proceed to use the same weights of quarters to create an $\bar{x}$ chart. The textbook explains that an $\bar{x}$ chart is used to monitor the *mean* of the process. It is obtained by plotting the sample means. Follow these steps to generate an $\bar{x}$ chart.

Minitab Procedure for Generating an $\bar{x}$ Chart

1. Enter all of the data in sequential order in column C1.

2. Select **Stat** from the main menu.

3. Select **Control Charts,** then select **Variable Charts for Subgroups.**

4. Select the option of **Xbar.**

5. Make these entries in the dialog box:

   • Enter C1 in the box for the column containing all observations.

   • Enter a subgroup size of 5 in the indicated box. (We use 5 here because the data in the table of weights includes 5 observations each day.)

   • Click **Xbar options**, click the **Estimate** tab, and click on the **Rbar** button.

   • Click **OK,** then click **OK** on the main dialog box.

Using the data in the table of weights of minted quarters given earlier, the Minitab display will be as shown below.

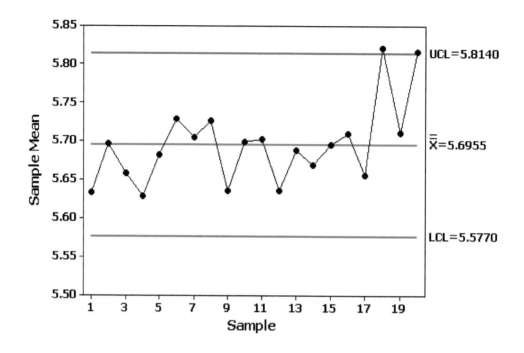

We can interpret the $\bar{x}$ chart by applying the three out-of-control criteria given in the textbook. We conclude that the mean in this process is *out of statistical control* because there is at least one point lying beyond the upper control limit.

14-4 *p* Charts

A control chart for attributes (or *p* chart) can also be constructed by using the same procedure for *R* charts and $\bar{x}$ charts. A *p* chart is very useful in monitoring some process proportion, such as the proportions of defects over time. Listed below are the numbers of defects in batches of 10,000 randomly selected each day from a new manufacturing process that is being tested.

Defects: 8 7 12 9 6 10 10 5 15 14 12 14 9 6 16 18 20 19 18 24

Follow these steps to generate a Minitab *p* chart:

Minitab Procedure for Generating a *p* Chart

    1. Enter the numbers of defects (or items with any particular attribute) in column C1.

    2. Select the main menu item of **Stat**.

    3. Select the subdirectory item of **Control Charts**.

    4. Select the option of **Attribute Charts**.

    5. Select the option of **P**.

    6. Make these entries in the dialog box:

- Enter C1 in the box labeled Variable.

- Enter the subgroup size. (For example, if C1 consists of the numbers of defects per batch and each batch consists of 10,000 quarters, then enter 10000 for the subgroup size.)

- Click **OK**.

The Minitab display will be as shown below. We can interpret the control chart for *p* by considering the three out-of-control criteria listed in the textbook. Using those criteria, we conclude that this process is out of statistical control for this reason: There appears to be an upward trend; also, there is a point lying beyond the upper control limit. Immediate action should be taken to correct the increasing proportion of defects.

CHAPTER 14 EXPERIMENTS: Statistical Process Control

Constructing Control Charts for Aluminum Cans. *Experiments 1 and 2 are based on the axial loads (in pounds) of aluminum cans that are 0.0109 in. thick, as listed in the "Aluminum Cans" data set in Appendix B of the textbook. An axial load of a can is the maximum weight supported by its side, and it is important to have an axial load high enough so that the can isn't crushed when the top lid is pressed into place. The data are from a real manufacturing process, and they were provided by a student who used an earlier version of this book.*

14–1. ***R Chart***   On each day of production, seven aluminum cans with thickness 0.0109 in. were randomly selected and the axial loads were measured. The ranges for the different days are listed below, but they can also be found from the values given in the data set from Appendix B of the textbook. Construct an *R* chart and determine whether the process variation is within statistical control. If it is not, identify which of the three out-of-control criteria lead to rejection of statistically stable variation.

> 78 77 31 50 33 38 84 21 38 77 26 78 78
> 17 83 66 72 79 61 74 64 51 26 41 31

14–2. ***x̄ Chart***   On each day of production, seven aluminum cans with thickness 0.0109 in. were randomly selected and the axial loads were measured. The means for the different days are listed below, but they can also be found from the values given in the dataset from Appendix B of the textbook. Construct an *x̄* chart and determine whether the process mean is within statistical control. If it is not, identify which of the three out-of-control criteria lead to rejection of statistically stable variation.

> 252.7 247.9 270.3 267.0 281.6 269.9 257.7 272.9 273.7 259.1
> 275.6 262.4 256.0 277.6 264.3 260.1 254.7 278.1 259.7 269.4
> 266.6 270.9 281.0 271.4 277.3

Energy Consumption. *In Experiments 14-3 through 14-5, use the following amounts of electricity consumed (in kWh) in the author's home. Let each subgroup consist of the six amounts within the same year, so that there are eight subgroups with six amounts in each subgroup.*

Year 1	3637	2888	2359	3704	3432	2446
Year 2	4463	2482	2762	2288	2423	2483
Year 3	3375	2661	2073	2579	2858	2296
Year 4	2812	2433	2266	3128	3286	2749
Year 5	3427	578	3792	3348	2937	2774
Year 6	3016	2458	2395	3249	3003	2118
Year 7	4261	1946	2063	4081	1919	2360
Year 8	2853	2174	2370	3480	2710	2327

14-3. ***Energy Consumption: R Chart*** Let each subgroup consist of the 6 values within a year. Construct an *R* chart and determine whether the process variation is within statistical control. If it is not, identify which of the three out-of-control criteria lead to rejection of statistically stable variation.

14-4. ***Energy Consumption: x̄ Chart*** Let each subgroup consist of the 6 values within a year. Construct an *x̄* chart and determine whether the process mean is within statistical control. If it is not, identify which of the three out-of-control criteria lead to rejection of a statistically stable mean.

14-5. ***Energy Consumption: Run Chart*** Construct a run chart for the 48 values. Does there appear to be a pattern suggesting that the process is not within statistical control?

14-6. ***p Chart for Defective Defibrillators*** Consider a process that includes careful testing of each manufactured defibrillator. Listed below are the numbers of defective defibrillators in successive batches of 10,000. Construct a control chart for the proportion *p* of defective defibrillators and determine whether the process is within statistical control. If not, identify which of the three out-of-control criteria apply.

Defects: 20 14 22 27 12 12 18 23 25 19 24 28 21 25 17 19 17 22 15 20

14-7. ***p Chart for Defective Defibrillators*** Repeat the preceding exercise assuming that the size of each batch is 100 instead of 10,000. Compare the control chart to the one found for the preceding exercise. Comment on the general quality of the manufacturing process described in the preceding exercise compared to the manufacturing process described in this exercise.

14-8. ***Violent Crimes*** In each of recent and consecutive years, 100,000 people in the United States were randomly selected and the number who were victims of violent crime was determined, with the results listed below. Does the rate of violent crime appear to exhibit acceptable behavior? (The values are based on data from the U.S. Department of Justice.) How does the result affect us?

685 637 611 566 523 507 505 494 476 463 469 474 458 429

14-9. ***Cola Cans*** In ach of several consecutive days of production of cola cans, 500 cans are tested and the numbers of defects each day are listed below. What action should be taken?

20 22 19 17 19 15 16 13 14 14 11 13 12 11 10 9 9 10 7 7

Minitab Release 17
Important Menu Items

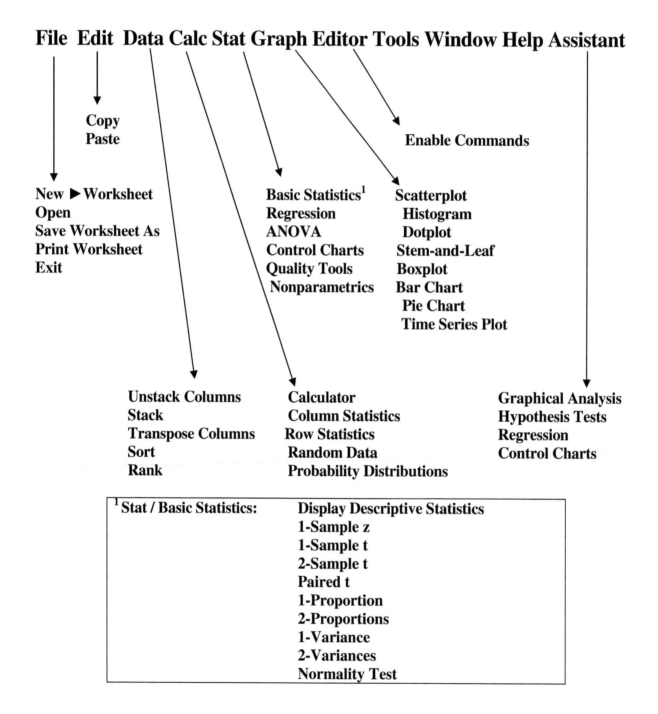

File Edit Data Calc Stat Graph Editor Tools Window Help Assistant

Copy
Paste

Enable Commands

New ▶ Worksheet   **Basic Statistics[1]**   **Scatterplot**
Open   **Regression**   **Histogram**
Save Worksheet As   **ANOVA**   **Dotplot**
Print Worksheet   **Control Charts**   **Stem-and-Leaf**
Exit   **Quality Tools**   **Boxplot**
                              Nonparametrics   **Bar Chart**
                                                   Pie Chart
                                                   Time Series Plot

Unstack Columns   **Calculator**   **Graphical Analysis**
Stack   **Column Statistics**   **Hypothesis Tests**
Transpose Columns   **Row Statistics**   **Regression**
Sort   **Random Data**   **Control Charts**
Rank   **Probability Distributions**

[1] Stat / Basic Statistics:	Display Descriptive Statistics
	1-Sample z
	1-Sample t
	2-Sample t
	Paired t
	1-Proportion
	2-Proportions
	1-Variance
	2-Variances
	Normality Test

Appendix B Data Sets

Appendix B in the textbook provides descriptions of the datasets and lists the first five rows of data. The complete datasets can be downloaded from the website www.TriolaStats.com.

Data Set 1:   **Body Data**
Data Set 2:   **Foot and Height**
Data Set 3:   **Body Temperatures**
Data Set 4:   **Births**
Data Set 5:   **Family Heights**
Data Set 6:   **Freshman 15**
Data Set 7:   **IQ and Lead**
Data Set 8:   **IQ and Brain Size**
Data Set 9:   **Bear Measurements**
Data Set 10:   **Manatee Deaths**
Data Set 11:   **Alcohol and Tobacco in Movies**
Data Set 12:   **Passive and Active Smoke**
Data Set 13:   **Cigarette Contents**
Data Set 14:   **Oscar Winner Age**
Data Set 15:   **Presidents**
Data Set 16:   **Nobel Laureates and Chocolate**
Data Set 17:   **Course Evaluations**
Data Set 18:   **Speed Dating**
Data Set 19:   **Car Crash Tests**
Data Set 20:   **Car Measurements**
Data Set 21:   **Earthquakes**
Data Set 22:   **Tornadoes**
Data Set 23:   **Old Faithful**
Data Set 24:   **Word Counts**
Data Set 25:   **Fast Food**
Data Set 26:   **Cola Weights and Volumes**
Data Set 27:   **M&M Weights**
Data Set 28:   **Chocolate Chip Cookies**
Data Set 29:   **Coin Weights**
Data Set 30:   **Aluminum Cans**
Data Set 31:   **Garbage Weight**
Data Set 32:   **Airport Data Speeds**

Index